Jesus

Fathered by no man
Teacher to all men

Gentle revolutionary
proclaiming love
Worker of miracles

Prophesier of his own death
Executed by the Romans

He came back from the dead

Who was he?

'I am the way,' he said, 'no one
comes to the Father, but by me.'

This is the true story of the life
of Jesus Christ.

The Real Jesus

Scripture Union

47 Marylebone Lane London W1M 6AX

Contents

Superstar? Revolutionary? Or God?

Most of us, the moment we read or hear the name Jesus, assume that we know who is being referred to. But do we? Who, in fact, was Jesus?

In order to discover who he was, we need to find answers to a whole range of further questions: for example, when did he live—and where? Here, the answer is simple: two thousand years ago in Palestine.

But ask the question, 'What did Jesus really teach?' and we find conflicting answers. Was it revolution? Non-violence? Subversion? Submission? Do good, and it's pie in the sky when you die? Or take another question: what did he actually do? Did he love, hate, heal, harm, help or hinder people of his day who were looking for help with the problems of living? He was finally rejected—correct—but why? They gave him the most agonising and degrading death a criminal could suffer. Why? Is Jesus the Son of God? Is he alive today? Has he anything to offer post-literate, nuclear man?

Whatever the questions or the answers, three facts about Jesus stand out from among the statistics of our computerised society.

First, hundreds of millions of Bibles or portions of the Bible, are sold each year. The United Bible Societies circulation figure for 1975 was 303,467,307, and this does not include circulation by other publishers.

Second, more people are coming to believe in Jesus today than at any other time in history, and there is no sign of this phenomenon declining.

Third, the largest libraries in the world would find it difficult to contain all the books which have been written on Jesus, yet each year hundreds, if not thousands, of new titles are being published.

For some reason Jesus demands attention.

Who is Jesus? Superstar? Bearded revolutionary? Or is

he really God who entered his own world?

To such questions each individual must find answers for himself. But how? One thing is certain, the four Gospels in the Bible—Matthew, Mark, Luke and John—are actual historical records about Jesus Christ. They present the real Jesus, enabling each person to decide who he is for himself by reading the four Gospels. And it is on these records that this picture-strip book is based.

Our aim in producing this book is:

1. to give an introduction to the most amazing person and event this world has ever known, with the hope that all who read it will have an increased desire to find out more for themselves about the real Jesus;

2. to enable the reader to visualize the situations in which Jesus spoke and acted, and to understand more vividly the significance of his life, his trial, death and resurrection.

e Life of Jesus

MATTHEW, MARK, LUKE, AND JOHN

HE FIRST FOUR BOOKS OF THE NEW TESTAMENT ARE CALLED THE GOSPELS, WHICH MEANS "GOOD NEWS"--ABOUT JESUS: HIS LIFE, TEACHINGS, DEATH, AND URRECTION. BECAUSE THE BOOKS ARE ALIKE ANY WAYS, THE FACTS HAVE BEEN COMBINED E TO TELL ONE STORY.

TO EVERYONE, JESUS SAYS-- I AM THE WAY... NO ONE CAN COME TO GOD BUT BY ME.

FOR ALMOST SIXTY YEARS PALESTINE, THE HOME OF THE JEWS, HAS BEEN RULED BY THE MIGHTY ROMAN EMPIRE. TO MAINTAIN THEIR CONTROL, THE ROMANS APPOINTED HEROD, A CLEVER BUT CRUEL MAN, TO RULE THE LAND. THE JEWS HATE HIM-- AND THE ROMAN OFFICIALS WHO COME TO HIS COURT. THE TIME IS NOW 6 B.C....

HERE, OLD MAN, CARRY THIS FOR ME.

THAT CHEST IS TOO HEAVY FOR SUCH AN OLD MAN.

THE ROMANS DON'T CARE.

HOURS LATER THE OLD MAN REACHES HOME...

GRANDFATHER! WHAT'S THE MATTER?

A ROMAN SOLDIER MA... HIM CARRY... HEAVY CHE... TO HERO... PALAC...

11

THAT AFTERNOON -- AS THE JEWS IN JERUSALEM GATHER IN THE TEMPLE FOR PRAYER -- AN OLD PRIEST, ZACHARIAS, ENTERS THE HOLY PLACE TO PRAY AND OFFER INCENSE.

THIS IS THE GREATEST DAY IN MY LIFE. AFTER ALL THESE YEARS IT IS FINALLY MY TURN TO OFFER INCENSE ON GOD'S HOLY ALTAR.

HE STAYS SO LONG IN THE SECRET ROOM THAT THE PEOPLE BEGIN TO WONDER.

ZACHARIAS' PRAYER IS LONGER THAN THAT OF MOST PRIESTS.

HE IS A GOOD MAN. IT'S TOO BAD HE HAS NO SON TO TAKE HIS PLACE.

AT LAST ZACHARIAS COMES OUT AND FACES THE PEOPLE -- BUT HE CANNOT SPEAK!

WHAT HAPPENED IN THE HOLY PLACE OF GOD?

13

A SON! AND HE WILL PREPARE THE WAY FOR GOD'S CHOSEN ONE!

BUT, ZACHARIAS, WHY DO YOU WRITE THIS INSTEAD OF TELLING ME?

ZACHARIAS WRITES A SECOND MESSAGE AND GIVES IT TO HIS WIFE.

GOD FORGIVE ME. I DOUBTED THE ANGEL'S MESSAGE, AND HE TOLD ME I WOULD NOT BE ABLE TO SPEAK UNTIL THE MESSAGE CAME TRUE.

OVERJOYED--AND AWED BY THE GREAT TRUST GOD HAS PLACED IN THEM-- ZACHARIAS AND ELISABETH PREPARE FOR THE BIRTH OF THEIR SON. IN THE MONTHS THAT PASS THEY OFTEN READ TOGETHER THE PARTS OF SCRIPTURE THAT TELL ABOUT GOD'S PROMISES TO HIS PEOPLE.

AS THE AGED PRIEST AND HIS WIFE WAIT FOR THE COMING OF THEIR SON, THE ANGEL GABRIEL APPEARS TO ELISABETH'S COUSIN MARY, WHO IS ENGAGED TO JOSEPH, A CARPENTER, IN NAZARETH.

DO NOT BE AFRAID, MARY. GOD HAS CHOSEN YOU TO BE THE MOTHER OF HIS SON. HIS NAME WILL BE "JESUS." HE WILL BE A KING WHOSE REIGN WILL NEVER END.

I AM THE LORD'S SERVANT AND I WILL DO WHATEVER HE SAYS.

MARY TELLS NO ONE OF THE ANGEL'S MESSAGE, BUT IN A FEW DAYS SHE GOES TO THE CARPENTER SHOP TO SEE JOSEPH.

I HAVE DECIDED TO GO AND VISIT MY COUSIN, ELISABETH.

IN JUDAH? I HATE TO HAVE YOU GO ALONE, MARY. IF ONLY THE PERIOD OF OUR ENGAGEMENT WERE OVER AND WE WERE MARRIED, THEN I COULD TAKE YOU THERE.

SO, MARY LEAVES NAZARETH ALONE.

THE ANGEL SAID THAT ELISABETH IS GOING TO HAVE A SON, TOO. IT WILL BE GOOD TO TALK WITH HER.

AND WHEN SHE REACHES HER COUSIN...

MARY, HOW WONDERFULLY GOD HAS BLESSED YOU! BUT, TELL ME, WHY HAS THE MOTHER OF MY LORD COME TO VISIT ME?

FROM THIS GREETING MARY KNOWS THAT ELISABETH SHARES HER WONDERFUL SECRET. JOYFULLY SHE SINGS ALOUD HER PRAISE TO GOD.

MY SOUL DOTH MAGNIFY THE LORD... FOR HE THAT IS MIGHTY HATH DONE TO ME GREAT THINGS; AND HOLY IS HIS NAME.

15

A Father's Prophecy

FROM LUKE 1: 57-80; 2: 1-5

THE DAYS PASS SWIFTLY IN THE HOME OF THE OLD PR... ZACHARIAS. HIS WIFE, ELISA... AND HER YOUNG COUSIN, MAR... SPEND MANY HOURS TALKIN... ABOUT THE SONS GOD HAS PROMIS... THEM. WHEN ELISABETH AND ZACHARIA... CHILD IS BORN, NEIGHBORS AND RELATIVES COME TO SEE HIM.

HOW PROUD ZACHARIAS MUST BE TO HAVE A SON TO BEAR HIS NAME.

HE IS PROUD TO HAVE A SON, BUT THE CHIL... NAME JOHN.

JOHN? THEN YOU AREN'T NAMING HIM FOR ANYONE IN YOUR FAMILY?

ZACHARIAS -- WHO HAS NOT BEEN ABLE TO SPEAK A WORD SINCE HE DOUBTED THE ANGEL'S MESSAGE ABOUT THE BIRTH OF HIS SON -- MOTIONS FOR A TABLET. QUICKLY HE WRITES HIS ANSWER, AND HAND... IT TO THE WOMAN TO READ.

HIS NAME IS JOHN.

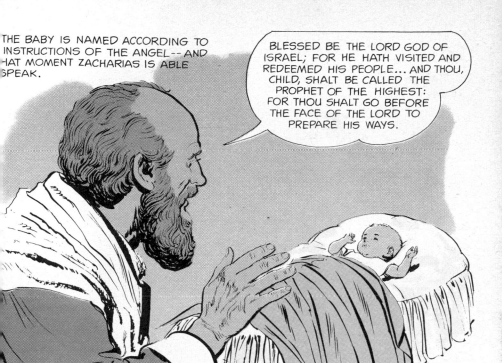

THE BABY IS NAMED ACCORDING TO
INSTRUCTIONS OF THE ANGEL-- AND
[T]HAT MOMENT ZACHARIAS IS ABLE
[TO] SPEAK.

BLESSED BE THE LORD GOD OF
ISRAEL; FOR HE HATH VISITED AND
REDEEMED HIS PEOPLE... AND THOU,
CHILD, SHALT BE CALLED THE
PROPHET OF THE HIGHEST:
FOR THOU SHALT GO BEFORE
THE FACE OF THE LORD TO
PREPARE HIS WAYS.

[ON] THEIR WAY HOME THE
[PEO]PLE TALK ABOUT THE
[STR]ANGE EVENTS CONNECTED
[WITH] THE BIRTH OF
[ZAC]HARIAS' SON.

THE
[N]AME JOHN
[--] WHAT DOES
[I]T MEAN?

IT MEANS,
"GOD HAS BEEN
GRACIOUS." GOD
MUST HAVE A
SPECIAL PURPOSE
FOR THAT CHILD.

HOME AGAIN IN NAZARETH, MARY THINKS ABOUT THE
PURPOSE GOD HAS FOR HER CHILD. BUT JOSEPH, THE
CARPENTER TO WHOM SHE IS ENGAGED, DOES NOT
UNDERSTAND WHAT THE ANGEL HAS TOLD MARY
ABOUT THE SON THAT IS TO BE BORN. ONE NIGHT AN
ANGEL COMES TO HIM.

GOD HAS CHOSEN MARY
TO BE THE MOTHER OF
HIS SON. YOU MUST CALL
THE CHILD JESUS, FOR
HE WILL SAVE HIS
PEOPLE FROM
THEIR SINS.

17

EARLY THE NEXT MORNING, JOSEPH HURRIES TO SEE MARY.

O MARY, IN A DREAM LAST NIGHT AN ANGEL TOLD ME THAT YOU ARE TO BE THE MOTHER OF THE LORD. I SEE NOW THAT GOD HAS CHOSEN ME TO TAKE CARE OF YOU AND YOUR SON.

SO MARY AND JOSEPH ARE MARRIED, AND MOVE INTO JOSEPH'S HOUSE BESIDE THE CARPENTER SHOP. IN THE EVENINGS WHEN THE DAY'S WORK IS DONE, THEY REST ON THE ROOF TOP--WATCHING THE STARS AND TALKING ABOUT GOD'S PROMISE TO MARY.

BUT ONE DAY JOSEPH COMES HOME FROM THE MARKET PLACE WITH BAD NEWS: CAESAR AUGUSTUS HAS ORDERED EVERYONE TO REGISTER HIS NAME AND PROPERTY. SINCE JOSEPH AND MARY ARE DESCENDANTS OF KING DAVID, JOSEPH MUST GO TO BETHLEHEM, THE CITY OF DAVID.

BUT I CAN'T GO NOW-- AND LEAVE YOU...

YOU MUST GO, JOSEPH, AND I'LL GO WITH YOU. DON'T WORRY--GOD WILL BE WITH US.

EAGER TO HAVE THE REGISTRATION OVER, THEY SET OUT. SOON OTHERS JOIN THEM ON THE WAY. BUT THE JOURNEY TAKES SEVERAL DAYS, AND AFTER A WHILE JOSEPH AND MARY FALL BEHIND-- UNTIL THEY ARE AMONG THE LAST TO REACH BETHLEHEM.

WE HAVE TRAVELED A LONG WAY AND MY WIFE IS VERY TIRED. I NEED A ROOM.

I'M SORRY, BUT BETHLEHEM IS CROWDED THESE DAYS. THERE'S NO ROOM HERE.

18

The Night the Angels Sang
FROM LUKE 1: 23-55

19

THAT SAME NIGHT SOME SHEPHERDS ARE WATCHING THEIR SHEEP ON THE HILLS OUTSIDE THE CITY. THEY TALK OF THE CROWDS THAT HAVE COME TO BETHLEHEM.

I'VE HEARD THAT CAESAR AUGUSTUS ORDERED THIS REGISTRATION SO THAT HE CAN COLLECT MORE TAXES. WILL WE NEVER BE FREE FROM THESE FOREIGN TYRANTS?

GOD HAS PROMISED US A DELIVERER. AND ALL MY LIFE I HAVE PRAYED THAT I WOULD LIVE TO SEE HIM.

SUDDENLY-- A GREAT LIGHT SHINE AROUND THE SHEPHERDS.

WHAT IS IT?

O GOD PROTEC US.

FEAR NOT; FOR I BRING YOU GOOD NEWS OF GREAT JOY FOR ALL THE PEOPLE. FOR TO YOU IS BORN IN THE CITY OF DAVID A SAVIOR, WHO IS CHRIST THE LORD. YOU WILL FIND THE BABY LYING IN A MANGER.

N THE SKY IS FILLED WITH A GREAT
IR OF ANGELS -- SINGING THEIR PRAISE
GOD.

ory to God in the highest,
and on earth peace, good
will toward men.

THE ANGELS LEAVE -- THE BEAUTIFUL LIGHT
DISAPPEARS. ONCE AGAIN IT IS DARK AND
STILL ON THE BETHLEHEM HILLS.

I CAN SCARCELY
BELIEVE WHAT I
HAVE SEEN AND
HEARD. GOD HAS
SENT OUR DELIVERER,
OUR SAVIOR--**TONIGHT**!

AND TO THINK
HE SENT HIS
ANGEL TO TELL
POOR SHEPHERDS
LIKE US!

HE ANGEL
ID WE WOULD
D THE SAVIOR
A MANGER.
T'S GO TO
THLEHEM
D SEE HIM.

EAGERLY -- AND WITH AWE AND WONDER -- THE SHEPHERDS
HURRY TO BETHLEHEM. INSIDE THE GATE THEY TURN
TOWARD THE INN...

LOOK -.-
THERE'S A
LIGHT IN THE
STABLE!

OUR SAVIOR
IS HERE! AND
I'M GOING TO
SEE HIM!

21

A King is Born

FROM LUKE 2:7, 16-20; MATTHEW 2:1-8

IT IS A STRANGE AND HOL[Y] NIGHT. WHILE THE CROWD[ED] CITY OF BETHLEHEM SLEEPS, [THE] SON OF GOD IS BORN. LOVING[LY] MARY WRAPS HER BABY IN SWADDLIN[G] CLOTHES AND LAYS HIM IN A MANGE[R,] AND THERE THE SHEPHERDS FIND HIM

AN ANGEL TOLD US THAT THE SAVIOR HAS BEEN BORN. MAY WE SEE HIM?

MARY NODS, AND JOSEPH TURNS THE LAMP A LITTLE SO THAT ITS LIGHT FALLS ON THE MANGER. REVERENTLY THE SHEPHERDS LOOK AT THE BABY JESUS.

O GOD, WE THANK THEE FOR SENDING OUR SAVIOR, AND FOR LETTING US SEE HIM.

QUIETLY, THE SHEPHERDS TURN AWAY

...D GO BACK TO THEIR FLOCKS, STILL PRAISING ...FOR WHAT HAS HAPPENED THAT NIGHT. AT ...SAME TIME IN A ...FAR TO THE EAST, ...MEN TALK ABOUT ...RANGE THING THEY ...JUST SEEN.

THAT NEW STAR-- IT'S BRIGHTER THAN ALL THE REST. IT MUST HAVE A SPECIAL MEANING.

IT IS A SIGN FROM GOD THAT THE GREAT KING OF THE JEWS HAS BEEN BORN.

LET US GO TO JERUSALEM AND FIND THE KING.

...R MONTHS OF TRAVEL, THE WISE MEN REACH ...USALEM.

WE HAVE COME TO WORSHIP THE ONE BORN TO BE KING OF THE JEWS. PLEASE TELL US WHERE WE CAN FIND HIM.

...MUST BE ...AKEN. NO ...HAS BEEN ...N HERE ...ENTLY.

WHEN THE WISE MEN INQUIRE AT THE PALACE, KING HEROD--WHO HAS COMMITTED MORE THAN ONE MURDER TO PROTECT HIS THRONE-- IS FRIGHTENED. HE CALLS FOR THE CHIEF PRIESTS AND SCRIBES.

IS THERE ANYTHING IN THE SACRED BOOKS TELLING ABOUT A BABY WHO WILL BECOME KING OF THE JEWS?

YES, THE SCRIPTURES SAY HE WILL BE BORN IN BETHLEHEM.

SECRETLY HEROD SENDS FOR THE WISE MEN AND ASKS THEM WHEN THEY SAW THE STAR AND HOW LONG IT TOOK THEM TO COME TO JERUSALEM. THEN HE SPEAKS VERY SLYLY.

LOOK FOR THE CHILD IN BETHLEHEM. WHEN YOU FIND HIM, COME BACK AND TELL ME WHERE HE IS SO THAT I MAY WORSHIP HIM, TOO.

AND WHEN I FIND THAT CHILD, I'LL KILL HIM. NO ONE IS GOING TO BE KING OF THE JEWS BUT ME!

ight in the Night

OM MATTHEW 2:9-14

OLLOWING HEROD'S INSTRUCTIONS, THE WISE
MEN SET OUT FOR BETHLEHEM. AS THEY
VE JERUSALEM, THEY AGAIN SEE THE STAR
Y HAD SEEN IN THE EAST. IT LEADS THEM
BETHLEHEM, AND THERE...

LOOK! THE STAR HAS STOPPED ABOVE THAT HOUSE!

OUR JOURNEY IS FINISHED! SOON WE'LL SEE THE CHILD WHO IS TO BE KING OF THE JEWS!

OPLE IN BETHLEHEM ARE SURPRISED TO SEE THE IMPORTANT-
OKING STRANGERS STOP BEFORE THE HOUSE WHERE JOSEPH AND
RY NOW LIVE. WHEN THE WISE MEN TELL THEIR REASON FOR
MING, THEY ARE INVITED INSIDE. THERE THEY KNEEL BEFORE
E BABY JESUS.

WE HAVE COME A LONG WAY TO WOR- SHIP THE ROYAL CHILD.

AND TO BRING HIM GIFTS OF GOLD, FRANKINCENSE, AND MYRRH.

THAT NIGHT AT THE INN THE WISE MEN MAKE PLANS FOR THEIR RETURN HOME.

I'M GLAD THAT WE CAN GO BACK TO JERUSALEM AND TELL KING HEROD WHERE HE CAN FIND THE BABY.

THE NEXT MORNING...

I HAD A DREAM—

SO DID I! IN MY DREAM GOD WARNED US NOT TO RETURN TO JERUSALEM BECAUSE HEROD IS JEALOUS AND WANTS TO KILL THE CHILD.

I HAD THE SAME DREAM! HEROD WILL FIND OUT NOTHING FROM US. WE'LL GO HOME BY ANOTHER ROUTE.

26

THE WISE MEN ARE NOT THE ONLY [?]S WHO ARE WARNED OF HEROD'S [?]ER. AN ANGEL OF GOD APPEARS TO [?]EPH, TOO...

MARY! AN ANGEL HAS TOLD ME WE MUST ESCAPE AT ONCE -- TO EGYPT. HEROD WANTS TO KILL JESUS.

KILL JESUS! OH, NO!

[?] THE MIDDLE OF THE NIGHT, [?]SEPH AND MARY WITH THE BABY [?]SUS STEAL QUIETLY OUT OF [?]E CITY.

IN JERUSALEM, HEROD WAITS FOR THE RETURN OF THE WISE MEN. WHEN THEY DO NOT COME, HE SUSPECTS THEY ARE TRYING TO PROTECT THE CHILD -- FROM HIM.

THAT CHILD WILL NEVER LIVE TO TAKE MY THRONE. I'LL KILL EVERY BABY IN BETHLEHEM BEFORE I LET HIM ESCAPE.

27

Boy in the Temple

FROM MATTHEW 2:16-23; LUKE 2:40-52

FEARING THAT THE BABY JESUS WILL TAKE HIS THRONE, HEROD ORDERS ALL BOY BABIES IN BETHLEHEM KILLED, BUT JOSEPH AND MARY ESCAPE WITH JESUS TO EGYPT. AFTER A FEW MONTHS, AN ANGEL TELLS JOSEPH THAT HEROD IS DEAD AND THAT IT IS NOW SAFE TO TAKE JESUS HOME. IN NAZARETH...

MARY! AND JOSEPH! HOW GOOD TO HAVE YOU BACK. WHAT IS THE BABY'S NAME?

HIS NAME IS JESUS

JESUS. THE NAME MEANS "GOD SAVES." WE NEED SOMEONE TO SAVE US FROM THE TYRANTS WHO RULE PALESTINE.

...OSEPH SETS UP HIS CARPENTER SHOP--AND ...S THE YEARS PASS, JESUS LEARNS TO HELP ...M. WHEN THE DAY'S WORK IS OVER JESUS ...STENS TO THE ELDERS OF THE TOWN...

IN THE DAYS OF KING DAVID, **WE** WERE THE RULERS.

YES, BUT IN THOSE DAYS PEOPLE OBEYED GOD. TODAY, TOO MANY IGNORE HIS LAWS.

BUT JOSEPH AND MARY OBEY GOD'S COMMANDMENTS, AND TEACH JESUS TO OBEY THEM, TOO. EACH SPRING THEY ATTEND THE PASSOVER FEAST IN JERU- SALEM TO THANK GOD FOR DELIVERING THEIR ANCESTORS FROM SLAVERY IN EGYPT. IN THE CARAVAN THAT MAKES THE ANNUAL JOURNEY FROM NAZARETH, THERE IS NO ONE MORE EXCITED THAN JESUS.

...S YEAR, AS HE WORSHIPS IN THE ...PLE, JESUS THINKS OF MANY ...ESTIONS HE WOULD LIKE TO ASK ...E TEACHERS OF THE JEWS.

AFTER THE FEAST IS OVER, THE PEOPLE SET OUT FOR THEIR HOMES. THAT NIGHT WHEN THEY MAKE CAMP...

JOSEPH, WHERE IS JESUS?

HE'S WITH HIS FRIENDS. I'LL FIND HIM.

BUT NO ONE HAS SEEN JESUS. FRANTICALLY, JOSEPH AND MARY TURN BACK TO JERUSALEM. THEY SEARCH THE INNS, THE CROWDED STREETS, AND FINALLY THE TEMPLE.

JESUS! WE HAVE BEEN LOOKING FOR YOU EVERYWHERE.

BUT, MOTHER, DIDN'T YOU KNOW THAT I WOULD BE IN MY FATHER'S HOUSE?

WE ARE SURPRISED AT YOUR SON'S KNOWLEDGE OF THE SCRIPTURES. HIS QUESTIONS SHOW THAT HE HAS THOUGHT A GREAT DEAL ABOUT GOD AND HIS LAWS FOR MAN.

JESUS IS NO LIKE ANYONE ELSE. EVEN I, HIS MOTHER, DO NOT UNDERSTAND EVERYTHING ABOU HIM.

JESUS RETURNS WITH JOSEPH AND MARY TO NAZARETH, WHERE HE LIVES UNTIL HE IS 30 YEARS OLD. HE GROWS TALL AND STRONG, AND IS WELL LIKED BY THE PEOPLE OF NAZARETH. GOD IS ALSO PLEASED WITH HIM. SEVENTY MILES AWAY, IN THE WILDERNESS NEAR THE DEAD SEA, A MAN OF THE SAME AGE PREPARES FOR AN ASSIGNMENT THAT WAS PLANNED FOR HIM -- EVEN BEFORE HE WAS BORN.

Tempted!

ROM LUKE 3:1—4:4

AS SOON AS JOHN, THE COUSIN OF JESUS, IS OLD ENOUGH TO UNDERSTAND, HIS FATHER TELLS HIM: "BEFORE YOU WERE BORN, GOD PLANNED FOR YOU TO SERVE HIM IN A SPECIAL WAY." JOHN GROWS UP PREPARING TO SERVE GOD. AND AFTER THE DEATH OF HIS PARENTS HE GOES INTO THE WILDERNESS TO PRAY AND STUDY. THERE GOD CALLS HIM TO BEGIN HIS WORK.

O GOD, I'M READY TO PREPARE THE WAY FOR THE COMING OF THE SAVIOR.

HN PUTS HIS WORDS INTO ACTION D BEGINS PREACHING ALONG THE RDAN RIVER.

REPENT OF YOUR SINS AND BE BAPTIZED, FOR GOD'S KINGDOM IS CLOSE AT HAND.

31

NEWS SPREADS FAR AND WIDE ABOUT THE MAN WHO LOOKS AND SPEAKS LIKE A PROPHET OF OLD. CROWDS COME OUT FROM JERUSALEM TO HEAR THE MAN CALLED JOHN THE BAPTIST. SOME ARE ONLY CURIOUS, BUT JOHN KNOWS THEIR THOUGHTS.

THE SCOFFERS TURN AWAY, BUT MANY PEOPLE LISTEN EAGERLY. ONE DAY A CROWD GATHERS AT THE JORDAN RIVER.

DO YOU THINK THAT JUST BECAUSE YOU ARE JEWS YOU WILL BE ALLOWED IN GOD'S KINGDOM? NO, YOU MUST REPENT--

ARE YOU THE SAVIOR GOD HAS PROMISED US?

NO. I BAPTIZE WITH WATER, BU HE WILL BAPTIZE WITH THE HOLY SPIRIT OF GOD. PREPARE YOURSELVE THE SAVIOR IS COMING!

UNKNOWN TO JOHN, THE VERY ONE HE IS TALKING ABOUT IS IN THE CROWD. JESUS HAS COME DOWN FROM NAZARETH TO HEAR HIM. HE ASKS TO BE BAPTIZED.

IT IS GOOD, JOHN, FOR US TO SHOW THAT WE BELONG TO GOD'S KINGDOM.

WHY DO YOU COME TO ME FOR BAPTISM? IT IS I WHO NEED TO BE BAPTIZED BY YOU.

JOHN BAPTIZES JESUS.
D WHEN JESUS COMES UP
T OF THE WATER, THE SPIRIT
GOD DESCENDS LIKE A
VE UPON HIM. THEN A
CE FROM HEAVEN SPEAKS:

THIS IS MY BELOVED SON IN WHOM I AM WELL PLEASED.

THE CROWDS DO NOT UNDERSTAND WHAT HAS HAPPENED -- THEY GO HOME, NOT REALIZING THAT THEY HAVE SEEN THEIR SAVIOR. JOHN CONTINUES PREACHING -- REPENT OF YOUR SINS, FOR THE KINGDOM OF GOD IS COMING SOON.

TO JESUS, THE WORDS OF HIS
ATHER ARE A SIGN OF APPROVAL,
ND THE GIFT OF THE HOLY SPIRIT
S AN ASSURANCE OF HELP FOR
HE WORK GOD HAS SENT HIM TO DO.
E GOES INTO THE WILDERNESS --
LONE -- TO THINK ABOUT HIS PLAN
OR ESTABLISHING GOD'S KINGDOM.

AT THE END OF FORTY DAYS,
US IS HUNGRY. AS HE THINKS
FOOD, HE HEARS THE VOICE
THE DEVIL TEMPTING
TO USE HIS DIVINE
VER FOR HIS OWN
EFIT. "IF YOU ARE
LLY THE SON OF
, " THE DEVIL SAYS,
RN THIS STONE
 BREAD. AFTER
 GOD WOULD NOT
T HIS BELOVED
 TO BE HUNGRY. "

SCRIPTURE SAYS, "MAN SHALL NOT LIVE BY BREAD ALONE, BUT BY THE WORD OF GOD."

THE DEVIL DOESN'T GIVE UP EASILY. HE TRIES AGAIN -- AND THIS TIME WITH A MORE POWERFUL TEMPTATION ...

Victory in the Wilderness

To PREVENT JESUS FROM CARRYING OUT GOD'S WORK, THE DEVIL TEMPTS HIM TO SEEK EARTHLY POWERS FOR HIMSELF. BUT JESUS REFUSES. THE DEVIL TRIES AGAIN--THIS TIME HE TEMPTS JESUS TO MAKE HIMSELF POPULAR BY DOING SOMETHING SENSATIONAL.

"LET PEOPLE SEE YOUR DIVINE POWER BY THROWING YOURSELF FROM THE ROOF OF THE TEMPLE," THE DEVIL SAYS. "FOR, IF YOU ARE THE SON OF GOD, HIS ANGELS WILL TAKE CARE OF YOU."

THE SCRIPTURES SAY, "THOU SHALT NOT TEMPT GOD."

Having REJECTED EVERY TEMPTATION, JESUS LEAVES THE WILDERNESS AND GOES BACK TO BETHANY BEYOND THE JORDAN.

AS JESUS ENTERS BETHANY, JOHN THE BAPTIST POINTS HIM OUT TO TWO OF HIS OWN DISCIPLES — ANDREW AND JOHN.

THERE IS THE SAVIOR I HAVE BEEN TELLING YOU ABOUT.

THE TWO MEN TURN AND QUICKLY FOLLOW JESUS.

MASTER-- MAY WE TALK WITH YOU?

YES, COME WITH ME TO MY LODGING PLACE.

LISTENING TO JESUS IS SUCH A WONDERFUL EXPERIENCE THAT HOURS GO BY BEFORE ANDREW SUDDENLY REMEMBERS...

MY BROTHER! HE CAME DOWN HERE FROM CAPERNAUM WITH ME TO HEAR JOHN THE BAPTIST. I MUST FIND HIM AND BRING HIM TO SEE YOU.

ANDREW RUNS TO THE HOUSE WHERE HE AND HIS BROTHER ARE STAYING.

SIMON! I HAVE FOUND THE SAVIOR!

SIMON EAGERLY FOLLOWS ANDREW BACK THROUGH THE WINDING STREETS OF BETHANY.

THIS IS SIMON, MY BROTHER.

YES, YOU ARE SIMON, BUT FROM NOW ON YOU SHALL BE CALLED PETER, BECAUSE YOU WILL BE LIKE A ROCK.

THE NEXT DAY JESUS GOES NORTH TO GALILEE. HE INVITES ANOTHER YOUNG MAN, PHILIP, TO BE HIS DISCIPLE AND GO WITH HIM.

PHILIP ACCEPTS JESUS' INVITATION. LIKE ANDREW, HE WANTS TO SHARE HIS GOOD NEWS, SO HE HURRIES TO TELL A FRIEND.

NATHANAEL--COME WITH ME! I HAVE FOUND THE SAVIOR! HE IS JESUS OF NAZARETH.

NAZARETH? CAN ANYTHING GOOD COME FROM **THAT** TOWN?

IF WHAT YOU SAY IS TRUE, MEN WOULD GIVE UP EVERYTHING THEY HAVE TO FOLLOW HIM.

COME AND SEE FOR YOURSELF!

NATHANAEL SEES JESUS, BUT HE STILL DOESN'T BELIEVE. THEN JESUS SPEAKS

PHILIP IS SO EXCITED ABOUT SEEING JESUS THAT HE HURRIES TO TELL A FRIEND. "NATHANAEL, COME WITH ME. I HAVE FOUND THE SAVIOR!" NATHANAEL DOUBTS SUCH NEWS, BUT HE AGREES TO SEE FOR HIMSELF. AS THEY APPROACH JESUS...

BEHOLD, A MAN IN WHOM THERE IS NOTHING DECEITFUL.

HOW DO **YOU** KNOW ANYTHING ABOUT ME?

BEFORE PHILIP CALLED YOU, YOU WERE SITTING UNDER A FIG TREE THINKING ABOUT GOD. I SAW YOU THERE.

YOU **ARE** THE SAVIOR FOR WHOM WE HAVE WAITED SO LONG!

HAVING FOUND HIS SAVIOR, NATHANAEL FORGETS EVERY-THING ELSE AND JOINS JESUS AND HIS FRIENDS AS THEY TRAVEL NORTH TO GALILEE. AT THE CROSSROADS, PETER AND ANDREW TURN OFF TO THEIR HOME NEAR THE SEA OF GALILEE; THE OTHERS GO ON TO CANA.

WHEN THEY REACH THE TOWN THEY ARE GREETED BY A FRIEND OF JESUS.

PLEASE COME TO MY WEDDING FEAST -- YOUR MOTHER WILL BE THERE.

THANK YOU -- WE WOULD LIKE TO SHARE YOUR HAPPINESS.

DURING THE FEAST MARY DISCOVERS SOMETHING THAT WILL EMBARRASS THE GROOM -- THERE IS NO MORE WINE. SHE TELLS JESUS, THEN SHE GOES TO THE SERVANTS.

DO WHATEVER HE TELLS YOU.

FILL THESE JARS WITH WATER.

WHY WATER? IT'S WINE WE NEED.

BUT THE SERVANTS SENSE A STRANGE AUTHORITY IN JESUS, AND THEY OBEY HIM.

NOW TAKE SOME TO THE HEADWAITER.

WHY -- IT IS WINE! IT'S A MIRACLE!

THIS MAN MUST BE A PROPHET OF GOD -- NO ORDINARY MAN COULD DO SUCH A THING!

THE HEADWAITER IS SO SURPRISED WHEN HE TASTES THE WINE THAT HE CALLS THE GROOM AWAY FROM THE FEAST.

SIR, THE BEST WINE IS USUALLY SERVED FIRST. BUT YOU HAVE SAVED THE BEST TO THE LAST.

I'M GLAD IF PEOPLE ARE HAPPY.

WHEN JESUS' DISCIPLES HEAR ABOUT THE MIRACLE, THEY TOO ARE EXCITED. THEY TALK ABOUT IT AS THEY GO DOWN TO JERUSALEM WITH JESUS FOR THE PASSOVER FEAST. THE CITY IS CROWDED WITH PEOPLE WHO HAVE HEARD JOHN THE BAPTIST TELL ABOUT THE COMING OF THE MESSIAH. "HOW WILL WE RECOGNIZE HIM?" THEY ASK.

JESUS WALKS THROUGH THE BUSY STREETS, HEALS THE LAME AND THE SICK.

I CAN WALK! PRAISE BE TO GOD -- THIS MAN HEALED ME!

BECAUSE OF THESE MIRACLES, PEOPLE BEGIN TO ASK: "IS JESUS THE MESSIAH?" ONE NIGHT, AFTER THE STREETS ARE EMPTY, A JUDGE OF THE JEWISH SUPREME COURT STEALS THROUGH THE STREETS OF JERUSALEM ON A SECRET MISSION.

The Judge's Problem

FROM JOHN 3:3—4:6

NICODEMUS, A JUDGE OF THE JEWISH SUPREME COURT, HAS A PROBLEM HE CAN'T SOLVE. PEOPLE IN JERUSALEM ARE ASKING, "IS JESUS THE SAVIOR WHO WILL OVERTHROW THE ROMANS AND SET UP GOD'S KINGDOM IN PALESTINE?" NICODEMUS ISN'T SURE, AND HE WONDERS: "WHAT MUST A MAN DO TO ENTER GOD'S KINGDOM?" HE HAS TO FIND OUT. SO SECRETLY-- BY NIGHT-- HE GOES TO THE PLACE WHERE JESUS IS STAYING, AND JESUS ANSWERS HIS QUESTION EVEN BEFORE HE ASKS IT...

A MAN MUST BE BORN OVER AGAIN TO ENTER GOD'S KINGDOM.

BORN AG... HOW CAN... BORN AG... WHEN I... OLD?

YOU WERE BORN ONCE OF EARTHLY PARENTS. BUT YOU MUST BE BORN AGAIN OF GOD'S SPIRIT TO LIVE IN GOD'S KINGDOM.

I DON'T UNDERSTAND.

YOU CAN'T SEE THE WIND, BUT YOU CAN SEE WHAT IT DOES. YOU CANNOT SEE THE SPIRIT OF GOD, BUT YOU CAN TELL BY THE WAY A MAN LIVES IF HE HAS BEEN BORN AGAIN AND HAS THE SPIRIT OF GOD IN HIS HEART. GOD LOVES THE WORLD, AND HE HAS SENT ME TO GIVE THIS NEW LIFE TO ALL WHO BELIEVE IN ME.

NICODEMUS GOES AWAY--STILL PUZZLED, BUT WANTING TO LEARN MORE ABOUT JESUS AND HIS TEACHINGS.

JESUS SEES THAT MANY OF THE PEOPLE IN JERUSALEM ARE NOT READY TO RECEIVE HIM AS THEIR SAVIOR, SO HE LEAVES THE CITY. IN JUDEA HE TELLS THE PEOPLE ABOUT GOD'S KINGDOM AND WHAT THEY MUST DO TO ENTER IT. HERE, THE PEOPLE LISTEN EAGERLY.

THIS TEACHER IS GREATER THAN ALL THE PROPHETS.

NEWS OF JESUS' SUCCESSFUL MINISTRY IN JUDEA REACHES JOHN THE BAPTIST.

I'VE HEARD THAT JESUS IS BECOMING MORE POPULAR EVERY DAY.

THANK GOD, I HAVE FULFILLED MY MISSION OF PREPARING THE WAY FOR HIM. JESUS' INFLUENCE MUST INCREASE, AND MINE DECREASE.

41

SOMETIME LATER JESUS RECEIVES NEWS ABOUT HIS LOYAL FRIEND.

HEROD HAS PUT JOHN THE BAPTIST IN PRISON FOR TRYING TO START A REVOLUTION.

REVOLUTION? NO-- THE REAL REASON IS THAT JOHN CONDEMNED HEROD FOR MARRYING HIS BROTHER'S WIFE.

SOON AFTER THIS, JESUS DECIDES TO EXTEND HIS MINISTR INTO ANOTHER ARE/ HE SETS OUT FOR GALILEE, NORTH O SAMARIA.

AS THEY APPROACH A TOWN IN SAMARIA, JESUS SENDS HIS DISCIPLES ON AHEAD TO BUY SOME FOOD.

IT MAY BE QUICKER TO GO TO GALILEE BY WAY OF SAMARIA, BUT I WONDER IF IT'S WISE. SAMARITANS HATE US JEWS.

WHILE JESUS IS RESTING BESIDE THE WELL, A WOMAN COMES UP WITH A JAR FOR WATER.

A JEW! DOESN'T HE KNOW JEWS AREN'T WELCOME IN SAMARIA?

WHEN JESUS TELLS HER THAT HE IS THE SAVIOR FROM GOD, SHE BELIEVES HIM AND RUNS BACK TO THE TOWN TO TELL THE WONDERFUL NEWS.

COME! SEE A MAN WHO HAS TOLD ME THINGS ABOUT MY LIFE THAT NO STRANGER COULD KNOW. HE IS THE PROMISED MESSIAH! THE SAVIOR!

WHILE THE WOMAN IS IN THE TOWN, JESUS DISCIPLES RETURN AND INVITE HIM TO SHARE THE FOOD THEY HAVE BOUGHT.

THANK YOU, BUT NOT NOW-- I HAVE FOOD THAT YOU DON'T KNOW ABOUT.

WHAT DO YOU MEAN?

MY FOOD IS TO DO THE WILL OF HIM WHO SENT ME. LOOK AT THE PEOPLE WHO ARE EAGER TO HEAR WHAT GOD HAS SENT ME TO TELL THEM.

ALTHOUGH THE SAMARITANS HATE JEWS, MANY OF THEM BELIEVE JESUS TO BE THEIR SAVIO "STAY," THEY PLEAD, "AND TELL MORE ABOUT GOD AND HIS KINGDOM." JESUS REMAINS FOR TWO DAYS -- THEN GOES ON TO THE REGION OF GALILEE.

ON THE SABBATH, IN HIS TOWN OF NAZARETH, HE GOES TO THE SYNAGOGUE. THERE HE READS FROM THE BOOK OF ISAIAH WHICH TELLS ABOUT THE COMING OF THE MESSIAH. THEN HE SITS DOWN TO TEACH.

TODAY THIS SCRIPTURE HAS BEEN FULFILLED IN YOUR EARS.

YOU -- THE MESSIAH? WHY, YOU'RE JUST THE SON OF A NAZARETH CARPENTER!

NO, PROPHET IS ACCEPTED IN HIS OWN COUNTRY. REMEMBER -- IN THE DAYS OF ELISHA THERE WERE MANY LEPERS IN ISRAEL, BUT THE PROPHET HEALED ONLY ONE -- A FOREIGNER, NAAMAN.

THE THOUGHT THAT GOD WOULD DO MORE FOR FOREIGNERS THAN FOR THEM -- HIS CHOSEN PEOPLE -- TURNS THE WORSHIPERS INTO AN ANGRY MOB.

DRIVE HIM OUT OF THE CITY!

KILL HIM!

On a Nazareth Hill

FROM LUKE 4:29-37; MARK 1:16-31; 2:1-3

THE MOB PUSHES
JESUS OUT OF
THE SYNAGOGUE...
THROUGH THE STREETS...
TO THE TOP OF A HILL.
IN ALL THAT TIME JESUS
MAKES NO MOVE TO
STOP THE ANGRY CROWD.

THROW HIM DOWN!

46

47

FATHER, WE MUST GO WITH JESUS AND HELP HIM IN THE WORK HE IS DOING FOR GOD.

GO, MY SONS, AND MAY GOD BLESS YOU.

WITH HIS DISCIPLES JESUS MAKES HIS HEADQUART IN CAPERNAUM. ON THE SABBATH HE GOES TO TH SYNAGOGUE--AND WHILE HE IS TEACHING, A MA POSSESSED BY AN EVIL SPIRIT CRIES OUT...

I KNOW WHO YOU ARE-- THE HOLY ONE OF GOD. HAVE YOU COME TO DESTROY ME?

JESUS FEELS SORRY FOR THE MAN AND ORDERS THE EVIL SPIRIT TO COME OUT OF HIM.

I DON'T KNOW--BUT I'VE HEARD HE CAN CHANGE WATER INTO WINE AND MAKE THE LAME WALK.

WHO IS THIS MAN WHO HAS POWER OVER EVIL SPIRITS?

LATER THAT DAY JESUS HEALS PETER'S MOTH IN-LAW, WHO HAS BEEN ILL WITH A FEVER. NE OF THESE MIRACLES SPREADS THROUGH TH COUNTRY, AND WHEREVER JESUS GOES GREA CROWDS FOLLOW HIM. ONE DAY IN CAPERNAUM

IT'S NO USE. YOU CAN NEVER GET ME THROUGH THAT MOB TO JESUS.

AND IF HE DOESN'T SEE JESUS, HE'LL NEVER BE WELL AGAIN.

hrough the Roof

OM MARK 2:1-12

VERYWHERE JESUS GOES THE CROWDS FOLLOW HIM. ONE DAY IN CAPERNAUM SO ANY PEOPLE CROWD INTO THE USE WHERE HE IS ACHING THAT NO ONE SE CAN ENTER. SOME EN WHO HAVE BROUGHT A CK FRIEND TO SEE JESUS NNOT GET THROUGH E CROWD, SO THEY RRY THE MAN TO E ROOF TOP.

MAKING A HOLE SO YOU CAN GET IN.

WHAT ARE YOU DOING?

AFTER A FEW MINUTES OF HARD WORK, THE SICK MAN IS LET DOWN THROUGH THE ROOF. JESUS IS PLEASED TO HELP, FOR HE KNOWS THE MAN'S REAL NEED.

YOUR SINS ARE FORGIVEN.

THE PEOPLE ARE AMAZED. BUT THE PHARISEES,* WHO HAVE COME OUT OF CURIOSITY TO HEAR JESUS, ARE ANGRY.

WHO IS THIS MAN WHO PRETENDS TO FORGIVE SINS?

HOW DARE HE ACT AS IF HE IS GOD!

*The Pharisees are a group of Jews who believe in obeying not only the laws God gave to Moses but the hundreds of rules they have made -- such as how far a man can walk on the Sabbath. Because Jesus is more concerned about helping people than obeying their rules, the Pharisees turn against him.

JESUS KNOWS WHAT THE PHARISEES ARE THINKING.

WHICH IS EASIER -- TO SAY TO THE SICK, "YOUR SINS ARE FORGIVEN," OR TO SAY, "ARISE, TAKE UP YOUR BED, AND WALK"?

BUT SO THAT ALL MAY KNOW THAT I HAVE DIVINE POWER TO DO BOTH, I SAY TO YOU, "ARISE, TAKE UP YOUR BED, AND GO TO YOUR HOME."

50

51

One Man's Answer

FROM MATTHEW 9: 9-13; 12: 9-14

IN ALL CAPERNAUM THERE IS NO JEW MORE DESPISED THAN MATTHEW, A TAX COLLECTOR FOR ROME. ONE DAY AS HE AND A MERCHANT ARE ARGUING ABOUT TAXES ON A CARAVAN OF GOODS, JESUS PASSES BY. HE LOOKS STRAIGHT INTO THE EYES OF THE HATED TAX COLLECTOR...

MATTHEW, FOLLOW ME.

THE AMAZEMENT OF THE CROWD, [MA]TTHEW TURNS FROM HIS WORK AND [FOL]LOWS JESUS.

[I] CAN'T BELIEVE IT! [MA]TTHEW IS GIVING [U]P HIS JOB TO GO [W]ITH A MAN OF GOD!

STRANGE -- NO GOOD JEW EVER WANTED MATTHEW FOR A FRIEND.

MATTHEW IS SO HAPPY TO START A NEW LIFE WITH JESUS THAT HE GIVES A BIG FEAST AND INVITES HIS FRIENDS TO MEET JESUS. SOME PHARISEES WHO ARE PASSING BY LOOK ON -- SURPRISED.

WHY DOES YOUR MASTER EAT WITH ALL THOSE SINNERS?

[JES]US ANSWERS FOR HIS DISCIPLE.

ONLY THE SICK NEED A DOCTOR. I HAVE COME NOT TO CALL THE RIGHTEOUS BUT SINNERS TO REPENT.

THE PHARISEES HAVE NO ANSWER TO THIS -- BUT IT MAKES THEM EVEN MORE ANGRY. SO EVERYWHERE JESUS GOES THEY WATCH FOR A CHANCE TO CRITICIZE HIM. ONE SABBATH DAY IN THE SYNAGOGUE...

LOOK -- JESUS IS TALKING TO THAT MAN WITH THE WITHERED HAND. LET'S SEE IF WE CAN CATCH HIM BREAKING A SABBATH LAW. THEN WE'LL HAVE A CASE AGAINST HIM.

mon on the Mount

LUKE 6: 12-16; MATTHEW 5; 6; 7; 8: 5-13; 13: 45, 46;
4: 35-37

Jesus KNOWS THAT THE PHARISEES ARE PLOTTING TO TAKE HIS LIFE, BUT HE DOES NOT LET THIS KEEP HIM FROM CARRYING ON THE WORK GOD SENT HIM TO DO. HE GOES TO A NEARBY MOUNTAIN -- AND SPENDS THE NIGHT IN PRAYER...

...AND FATHER, I THANK THEE FOR GUIDING ME IN THE CHOICES I HAVE MADE THIS NIGHT.

THE MORNING HE CALLS HIS DISCIPLES TO HIM -- AND FROM THE GROUP HE NAMES ELVE TO BE HIS FULL-TIME HELPERS: SIMON PETER, ANDREW, JAMES, JOHN, PHILIP, HANAEL BARTHOLOMEW, MATTHEW, THOMAS, JAMES THE SON OF ALPHEUS, THADDEUS, ON THE ZEALOT, AND JUDAS ISCARIOT. THESE ARE KNOWN AS THE TWELVE APOSTLES.

ON EALOT   JAMES SON OF ALPHEUS   MATTHEW PETER   JAMES NATHANAEL   JOHN   THOMAS PHILIP   JUDAS ANDREW   THADDEUS

As they come down the mountain they find a large crowd waiting for Jesus. So there--on the mountainside--Jesus preaches a sermon in which he explains what members of God's kingdom are like:

Blessed are the merciful: for they shall obtain mercy.
Blessed are the pure in heart: for they shall see God.
Blessed are the peacemakers: for they shall be called the children of God....

Ye are the light of the world.... Let your light so shine before men, that they may see your good works, and glorify your Father which is in heaven....

Love your enemies, bless them that curse you, do good to them that hate you, and pray for them which despitefully use you, and persecute you;

That ye may be the children of your Father which is in heaven: for he maketh his sun to rise on the evil and on the good, and sendeth rain on the just and on the unjust.

Therefore all things whatsoever ye would that men should do to you, do ye even so to them: for this is the law and the prophets.

(THE FULL SERMON FOUND IN MATTHE CHAPTERS 5, 6, 7.)

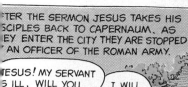

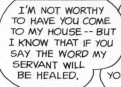

EVEN THOUGH THE PHARISEES ARE STILL PLOTTING AGAINST HIM, JESUS KEEPS ON TEACHING IN CAPERNAUM. ONE DAY THE CROWDS THAT COME TO HEAR HIM ARE SO GREAT THAT HE HAS TO GET INTO A BOAT AND PUSH OUT FROM SHORE IN ORDER TO TEACH THEM.

A MERCHANT ONCE SAW A RARE AND BEAUTIFUL PEARL. HE WANTED IT MORE THAN ANYTHING ELSE. SO HE SOLD EVERYTHING HE OWNED AND BOUGHT IT. THE KINGDOM OF GOD IS LIKE THAT PEARL -- IT IS WORTH EVERYTHING YOU HAVE TO POSSESS IT.

WHEN EVENING COMES JESUS SUGGESTS TO HIS DISCIPLES THAT THEY CROSS OVER TO THE OTHER SIDE OF THE LAKE.

IT'S THE KIND OF A NIGHT WHEN A SUDDEN STORM COULD HIT.

d Man by the Sea

MARK 4: 37-41; 5: 1-24, 35-43

IN TERROR THE DISCIPLES RUSH TO THE STERN OF THE BOAT.

MASTER! DON'T YOU CARE IF WE DROWN?

JESUS RISES AND FACES THE STORMY

PEACE, BE STILL!

INSTANTLY THE WIND DIES AND THE WAVES VANISH.

WHO IS HE, THAT EVEN THE WINDS AND THE SEA OBEY HIM?

IN THE MORNING THE BOAT REACHES SHORE; AN AS JESUS AND HIS DISCIPLES ARE WALKING UP BEACH, A MAN POSSESSED BY AN EVIL SPIRIT RUSH DOWN THE BANK TO MEET JESUS.

BE CARE HE'S BRO HIS CHAI

COME OUT OF THE MAN, THOU UNCLEAN SPIRIT.

THE MAN IS CURED -- THE PEOPLE WHO SEE IT ARE AMAZED, AND THEY WONDER, TOO, WHAT POWER JESUS HAS TO MAKE EVIL SPIRITS OBEY HIM.

LET ME GO WITH YOU.

IT WOULD BE BETTER IF YOU WENT HOME AND TOLD YOUR FRIENDS WHAT GOD HAS DONE FOR YOU.

...ER A WHILE JESUS AND HIS DISCIPLES ...URN TO CAPERNAUM. ONCE AGAIN A CROWD ...HERS TO HEAR HIM. BUT JUST AS JESUS ...INS TO TEACH, JAIRUS, THE CHIEF RULER ... THE SYNAGOGUE, PUSHES HIS WAY ...OUGH THE CROWD AND FALLS AT JESUS' FEET.

MY LITTLE GIRL — SHE'S DYING! PLEASE COME!

JESUS GOES WITH JAIRUS -- BUT ON THE WAY THEY ARE MET BY A SERVANT FROM JAIRUS' HOUSEHOLD...

IT'S TOO LATE -- YOUR DAUGHTER IS DEAD!

The Mocking Crowd

FROM MARK 5: 38-43; MATTHEW 9: 35—11: 1;
14: 1-12; JOHN 6: 1-10

WHEN JESUS AND HIS DISCIPLES REACH THE HOME OF JAIRUS, THEY FIND A CROWD OF PEOPLE WEEPING BECAUSE JAIRUS' DAUGHTER IS DEAD.

WHY ARE YOU CRYING? THE LITTLE GIRL IS JUST ASLEEP.

ASLEEP? HOW DARE YOU RAISE FALSE HOPE FOR THIS FAMILY? THE CHILD IS DEAD, AND EVERYONE KNOWS IT!

...ETLY JESUS LEADS THE CHILD'S PARENTS ...O HER ROOM. THERE HE TAKES THE GIRL'S ...ND AND SAYS, "ARISE." ...TANTLY SHE GETS UP-- ...O LOOKS AT JESUS IN ...PRISE AND WONDER.

GIVE HER SOMETHING TO EAT-- BUT DO NOT TELL ANYONE WHAT HAS HAPPENED IN THIS ROOM.

...UT JAIRUS IS AN ...PORTANT MAN. ...WS ABOUT HIS ...UGHTER SPREADS ...ICKLY. AND AS ...SUS TRAVELS ...ROUGH GALILEE, ...REACHING AND ...ALING, HIS FAME ...CREASES. THE ...ARISEES WATCH ...GRILY. AS YET ...EY HAVE NO REAL ...SE AGAINST ...SUS AND WITH- ...UT. ONE THEY ...RE NOT STIR UP ...E EXCITED CROWDS ...AT FOLLOW HIM.

BUT JESUS IS CONCERNED ABOUT THE MANY PEOPLE WHO STILL HAVE NOT HEARD HIS MESSAGE. HE CALLS HIS DISCIPLES ASIDE.

THE PEOPLE ARE LIKE SHEEP WITHOUT A SHEPHERD. I WANT YOU TO GO OUT BY TWOS TO PREACH AND HEAL THE SICK AS I HAVE DONE. DO NOT BE WORRIED ABOUT WHAT TO SAY, FOR THE SPIRIT OF GOD WILL SPEAK THROUGH YOU.

...DISCIPLES PREACH THROUGHOUT GALILEE. ...N THEY RETURN JESUS PREPARES TO TAKE ...M TO A QUIET PLACE TO REST AND TALK ABOUT ...RE PLANS. AS THEY ARE STARTING, A ...PLE OF JOHN THE ...IST BRINGS THEM ...IC NEWS.

JOHN HAS BEEN BEHEADED BY KING HEROD!

HEROD IS A WICKED MAN. BUT THIS IS THE WORST OF HIS SINS.

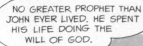

"NO GREATER PROPHET THAN JOHN EVER LIVED. HE SPENT HIS LIFE DOING THE WILL OF GOD."

SORROWFULLY, JESUS AND HIS DISCIPLES CROSS THE LAKE AND GO UP ON A MOUNTAINSIDE, HOPING TO BE ALONE. BUT A GREAT CROWD FOLLOWS THEM AND JESUS STOPS TO TEACH AND HEAL THE SICK. LATE IN THE AFTERNOON...

"PHILIP-- WHERE CAN WE BUY FOOD FOR THESE PEOPLE?"

"FOR **ALL** OF THEM? WHY, THERE MUST BE 5,000 MEN -- BESIDES THE WOMEN AND CHILDREN."

"HERE'S A BOY WITH FIVE LOAVES OF BREAD AND TWO FISHES -- BUT WHAT GOOD IS THAT FOR SUCH A CROWD?"

"HAVE THE PEOPLE SIT DOWN AND GIVE THE FOOD TO ME."

No Earthly Throne

ROM JOHN 6:10-15; MATTHEW 14:23-30

IT IS LATE AFTERNOON. THE CROWD THAT HAS FOLLOWED JESUS IS HUNGRY. BUT THE ONLY FOOD AVAILABLE BELONGS TO A BOY. HE EAGERLY GIVES IT TO JESUS, WHO THANKS GOD FOR IT AND HANDS IT TO HIS DISCIPLES.

DISTRIBUTE THE FOOD TO EVERYONE.

HOW FAR WILL FIVE LOAVES AND TWO FISHES GO IN FEEDING A CROWD OF OVER FIVE THOUSAND?

BUT THE DISCIPLES HAVE FAITH IN JESUS ... AND THEY OBEY HIM.

LOOK! EVERYONE HERE IS GETTING ALL THE FOOD HE WANTS.

IT'S A MIRACLE!

WHEN THE PEOPLE HAVE FINISHED EATING, JESUS TURNS AGAIN TO HIS DISCIPLES.

GATHER UP THE FOOD THAT REMAINS.

TWELVE BASKETS OF FOOD ARE LEFT OVER! THE PEOPLE ARE NOW MORE AMAZED THAN EVER.

MAYBE JESUS IS THE KING THE PROPHETS TALKED ABOUT.

A KING LIKE DAVID-- WHO WILL DESTROY OUR ENEMIES AND MAKE US RICH AND POWERFUL!

BUT GOD SENT JESUS TO BE THE SAVIOR, TO BRING MEN INTO THE KINGDOM OF GOD -- NOT TO COMMAND ARMIES AND CONQUER THRONES. WHEN JESUS SEES THAT THE CROWD WANTS TO FORCE HIM TO BE A KING, HE QUICKLY CALLS HIS DISCIPLES.

LAUNCH THE BOAT AND CROSS OVER TO THE OTHER SIDE OF THE SEA. I WILL JOIN YOU LATER.

QUICKLY -- BEFORE THE EXCITEMENT OF THE PEOPLE GROWS STRONGER -- JESUS DISMISSES THEM. THEN HE GOES UP ON A MOUNTAIN TO PRAY. LATER THAT NIGHT -- ON THE SEA OF GALILEE...

THE WIND IS RISING! WE'RE IN FOR A STORM!

Miracle on the Sea

FROM MATTHEW 14: 30-36; JOHN 6: 22-71;
MARK 7: 1-23; MATTHEW 16: 13-26; 17: 1, 2

A STRONG NIGHT WIND IS STIRRING UP ANGRY WAVES ON THE SEA OF GALILEE. JESUS' DISCIPLES ARE ROWING HARD AGAINST THE STORM -- WHEN SUDDENLY THEY SEE A FIGURE WALKING TOWARD THEM. THEY ARE TERRIFIED -- UNTIL THEY SEE THAT THE MAN ON THE WATER IS JESUS. PETER GETS OUT OF THE BOAT AND STARTS TOWARDS JESUS -- BUT WHEN HE SEES THE ROUGH WAVES HE LOSES FAITH...

O PETER, WHY DID YOU DOUBT?

LORD! SAVE ME!

JESUS RESCUES PETER, AND AS THEY REACH THE BOAT, THE WIND DIES, AND THE SEA IS CALM.

ONLY SOMEONE FROM GOD COULD DO WHAT JESUS HAS DONE!

AT DAYBREAK THE DISCIPLES BRING THE BOAT TO SHORE. WHEN THE PEOPLE SEE JESUS, THEY HURRY TO BRING THEIR SICK AND CRIPPLED TO HIM. PATIENTLY AND LOVINGLY HE HEALS THEM ALL.

IF ONLY I CAN TOUCH HIS GARMENT I KNOW I WILL BE HEALED.

LATER THAT DAY JESUS GOES TO THE SYNAGOGUE IN CAPERNAUM. THE CROWD THAT HE FED THE DAY BEFORE IS THERE ASKING TO BE FED AGAIN. WHEN JESUS PREACHES A SERMON ABOUT THEIR SPIRITUAL NEEDS, MANY OF THEM ARE DISAPPOINTED AND TURN AWAY.

SEEING THIS, THE PHARISEES RESUME THEIR PUBLIC CRITICISM OF JESUS.

WE HAVE SEEN YOUR DISCIPLES EAT WITHOUT WASHING THEIR HANDS. WHY DO YOU LET THEM BREAK OUR LAWS AND DEFILE THEMSELVES?

NOTHING A MAN PUTS **INTO** HIS MOUTH CAN DEFILE HIM, BUT THE EVIL WORDS THAT COME **OUT** OF HIS MOUTH DEFILE HIM.

SHOCKED BECAUSE HE DEFENDS HIS DISCIPLES, THE PHARISEES TURN AWAY, MORE DETERMINED THAN EVER TO DESTROY JESUS.

DON'T YOU KNOW THAT YOU HAVE MADE THE PHARISEES ANGRY?

THE PHARISEES ARE BLIND TO THE WILL OF GOD—AND THEY ARE LEADING THE PEOPLE TO BE AS BLIND AS THEY ARE.

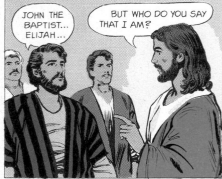

BECAUSE MOST OF THE PEOPLE WILL ACCEPT HIM ONLY AS AN EARTHLY KING, JESUS LEAVES GALILEE. HE TAKES HIS DISCIPLES TO THE COUNTRY OF PHENICIA—AND LATER TO THE REGION OF CAESAREA PHILIPPI, WHERE HE TEACHES THEM IN PRIVACY. THERE, ONE DAY, HE ASKS THEM: "WHO DO MEN SAY THAT I AM?"

JOHN THE BAPTIST... ELIJAH...

BUT WHO DO YOU SAY THAT I AM?

YOU ARE THE CHRIST, THE SON OF THE LIVING GOD.

BLESSED ARE YOU, PETER--FOR MY FATHER IN HEAVEN HAS REVEALED THIS TO YOU.

NOW THAT THE DISCIPLES TRULY UNDERSTAND THAT HE IS THE PROMISED MESSIAH, JESUS TELLS THEM WHAT WILL HAPPEN WHEN HE GOES TO JERUSALEM.

THE PHARISEES AND PRIESTS DO NOT BELIEVE THAT I AM THE MESSIAH. THEY WILL HAVE ME KILLED--BUT IN THREE DAYS I WILL RISE AGAIN.

71

A Boy—and His Father's Faith

FROM MATTHEW 17: 3-13; MARK 9: 33; LUKE 9: 37-45

ALONE WITH JESUS ON THE MOUNTAIN, PETER, JAMES AND JOHN SEE HIM TRANSFIGURED. HIS FACE SHINES WITH THE BRIGHTNESS OF THE SUN -- HIS CLOTHES BECOME DAZZLING WHITE. THEN TWO GREAT MEN OF THE PAST, MOSES AND ELIJAH, APPEAR TO TALK WITH HIM.

BUT AS PETER SPEAKS A BRIGHT CLOUD DESCENDS ON THE MOUNTAINTOP... AND OUT OF THE CLOUD COMES THE VOICE OF GOD:

THIS IS MY BELOVED SON, IN WHOM I AM WELL PLEASED; HEAR YE HIM.

...E DISCIPLES ARE SO
...RIGHTENED THAT THEY
...LL TO THE GROUND
...UT JESUS BENDS
...OWN AND TOUCHES
...HEM...

DO NOT BE AFRAID.

...HE NEXT MORNING-- ON
...THE WAY DOWN THE
...MOUNTAIN-- JESUS WARNS
...HIS DISCIPLES TO TELL
...NO ONE OF HIS TRANS-
...FIGURATION UNTIL AFTER
...HIS RESURRECTION.
...AFTER WHAT THEY HAVE
...JUST SEEN THE DISCIPLES
...CANNOT BELIEVE THAT
...ESUS WILL DIE -- SO
...THEY ARE PUZZLED
...WHEN JESUS TALKS ABOUT
...RISING FROM THE DEAD.

...THEY REACH THE VAL-
...EY TO FIND A GREAT
...CROWD GATHERED
...AROUND THE OTHER
...DISCIPLES.

AT THE SIGHT OF JESUS THE PEOPLE QUICKLY SURROUND HIM.

MY SON HAS SPELLS AND OFTEN FALLS INTO THE FIRE. I BROUGHT HIM TO YOUR DISCIPLES, BUT THEY COULD NOT HEAL HIM.

BRING YOUR SON TO ME.

...E FATHER OBEYS-- BUT THE BOY HAS A
...ELL AND FALLS TO THE GROUND AT JESUS' FEET.

IF YOU CAN HELP US-- PLEASE DO.

ALL THINGS ARE POSSIBLE TO ONE WHO HAS FAITH.

I BELIEVE! HELP ME, PLEASE, TO HAVE MORE FAITH.

THOU UNCLEAN SPIRIT-- COME OUT OF THE BOY!

FOR A MOMENT THERE IS A STRUGGLE -- THEN THE BOY BECOMES SO STILL PEOPLE THINK HE IS DEAD. BUT JESUS REACHES DOWN TO TAKE HIS HAND.

ARISE!

INSTANTLY THE BOY GETS UP.

FATHER, WHAT HAPPENED?

YOU HAVE BEEN HEALED -- BY THE POWER OF GOD!

WHEN THEY ARE ALONE, THE DISCIPLES TURN TO JESUS.

WHY COULDN'T **WE** HEAL THE BOY?

YOU DID NOT HAVE FAITH. IF YOU HAVE FAITH THE SIZE OF A MUSTARD SEED, NOTHING IS IMPOSSIBLE FOR YOU.

LATER ON THE WAY TO CAPERNAUM, THE DISCIPLES TALK AMONG THEMSELVES ABOU THE KINGDOM THEY EXPECT JESUS WILL SOC ESTABLISH. ALMOST AT ONCE THEY BEGIN TO QUARREL ABOUT WHICH ONE WILL BE THE GREATEST IN THAT KINGDOM.

IF ONLY **I** COULD SIT IN THE SEAT OF HONOR NEXT TO JESUS.

eventy Times Seven

FROM MATTHEW 18:1-14, 21, 22;
JOHN 7:11-52; 8:21-59

N THE WAY TO CAPERNAUM THE DISCIPLES
QUARREL ABOUT WHICH ONE OF THEM WILL BE
THE MOST IMPORTANT PERSON IN THE KINGDOM
EY EXPECT JESUS TO ESTABLISH. WHEN THEY
EACH THE CITY JESUS ASKS WHY THEY ARE
UARRELING AND THEY
RE ASHAMED TO SAY.
E CALLS A LITTLE
HILD TO HIM.

WHICHEVER ONE
OF YOU WANTS TO BE
GREATEST IN GOD'S
KINGDOM MUST BE AS
HUMBLE AND WILLING
TO LEARN AS THIS
LITTLE CHILD.

76

WHEN THE CHIEF PRIESTS AND PHARISEES HEAR WHAT THE PEOPLE ARE SAYING, THEY QUICKLY JOIN FORCES AGAINST JESUS.

IF WE DON'T GET RID OF HIM THE PEOPLE WILL ACCEPT HIM AS THE MESSIAH.

I'LL STOP HIM. CALL THE TEMPLE GUARDS.

ARREST JESUS. BUT DO IT AT A TIME WHEN IT WILL CAUSE THE LEAST TROUBLE.

ON THE LAST DAY OF THE FEAST THE OFFICERS RETURN TO THE PRIESTS AND PHARISEES.

WHERE IS JESUS?

WE'VE NEVER HEARD ANYONE SPEAK AS THIS MAN DOES. WE COULD NOT ARREST HIM.

THE PRIESTS AND PHARISEES ARE FURIOUS -- BUT THEY ARE AFRAID TO FORCE THE ISSUE WHILE THE CITY IS CROWDED WITH PEOPLE ATTENDING THE FEAST. BUT THE NEXT DAY...

JESUS RETURNS TO THE TEMPLE TO PREACH. IN THE COURSE OF HIS SERMON HE NOT ONLY POINTS OUT THE SINS OF THE PRIESTS AND PHARISEES BUT DECLARES THAT HE WAS WITH GOD EVEN BEFORE THE DAYS OF THEIR GREAT FOREFATHER, ABRAHAM.

HOW DARE HE CLAIM SUCH RELATIONSHIP WITH GOD!

STONE HIM! STONE HIM!

A Jerusalem Beggar Meets the Son of God

FROM JOHN 9:1—10:21; LUKE 10:25

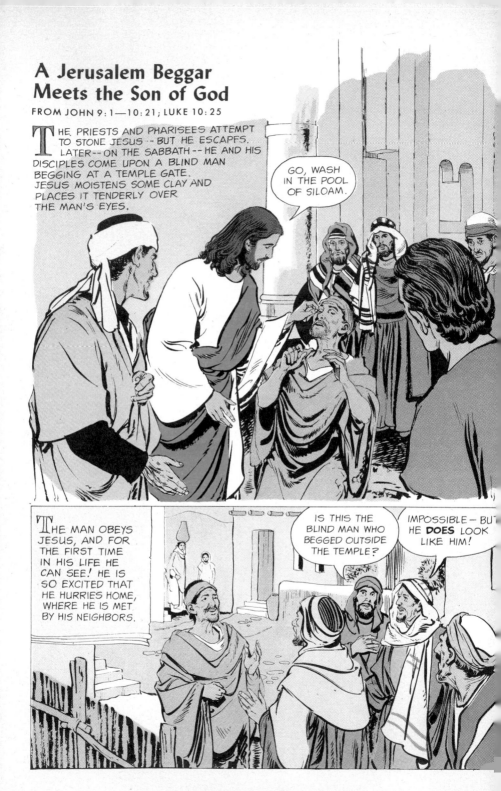

THE PRIESTS AND PHARISEES ATTEMPT TO STONE JESUS --BUT HE ESCAPES. LATER-- ON THE SABBATH -- HE AND HIS DISCIPLES COME UPON A BLIND MAN BEGGING AT A TEMPLE GATE. JESUS MOISTENS SOME CLAY AND PLACES IT TENDERLY OVER THE MAN'S EYES.

GO, WASH IN THE POOL OF SILOAM.

THE MAN OBEYS JESUS, AND FOR THE FIRST TIME IN HIS LIFE HE CAN SEE! HE IS SO EXCITED THAT HE HURRIES HOME, WHERE HE IS MET BY HIS NEIGHBORS.

IS THIS THE BLIND MAN WHO BEGGED OUTSIDE THE TEMPLE?

IMPOSSIBLE— BUT HE **DOES** LOOK LIKE HIM!

BUT **I AM** THE MAN WHO WAS BLIND. JESUS GAVE ME MY SIGHT!

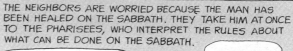

THE NEIGHBORS ARE WORRIED BECAUSE THE MAN HAS BEEN HEALED ON THE SABBATH. THEY TAKE HIM AT ONCE TO THE PHARISEES, WHO INTERPRET THE RULES ABOUT WHAT CAN BE DONE ON THE SABBATH.

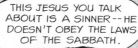

THIS JESUS YOU TALK ABOUT IS A SINNER -- HE DOESN'T OBEY THE LAWS OF THE SABBATH.

I DO NOT KNOW WHETHER HE IS A SINNER, BUT THIS I DO KNOW: I WAS BLIND AND NOW I SEE.

E PHARISEES TRY TO MAKE THE MAN TURN AINST JESUS, BUT THEY CANNOT, SO THEY PUT A OUT OF THE SYNAGOGUE. JESUS LEARNS AT HAS HAPPENED, AND SEARCHES FOR THE E MAN. WHEN HE FINDS HIM THE PHARISEES ICKLY GATHER AROUND.

O YOU BELIEVE IN HE SON OF GOD?

WHO IS HE -- THAT I MAY BELIEVE IN HIM?

I AM -- THE VERY ONE WHO IS SPEAKING TO YOU.

LORD, I BELIEVE!

79

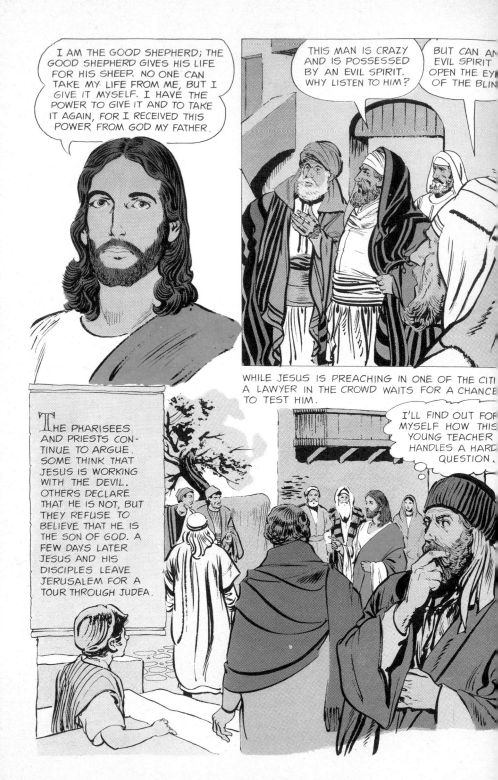

I AM THE GOOD SHEPHERD; THE GOOD SHEPHERD GIVES HIS LIFE FOR HIS SHEEP. NO ONE CAN TAKE MY LIFE FROM ME, BUT I GIVE IT MYSELF. I HAVE THE POWER TO GIVE IT AND TO TAKE IT AGAIN, FOR I RECEIVED THIS POWER FROM GOD MY FATHER.

THIS MAN IS CRAZY AND IS POSSESSED BY AN EVIL SPIRIT. WHY LISTEN TO HIM?

BUT CAN AN EVIL SPIRIT OPEN THE EY OF THE BLIN

WHILE JESUS IS PREACHING IN ONE OF THE CITI A LAWYER IN THE CROWD WAITS FOR A CHANCE TO TEST HIM.

THE PHARISEES AND PRIESTS CONTINUE TO ARGUE. SOME THINK THAT JESUS IS WORKING WITH THE DEVIL. OTHERS DECLARE THAT HE IS NOT, BUT THEY REFUSE TO BELIEVE THAT HE IS THE SON OF GOD. A FEW DAYS LATER JESUS AND HIS DISCIPLES LEAVE JERUSALEM FOR A TOUR THROUGH JUDEA.

I'LL FIND OUT FOR MYSELF HOW THIS YOUNG TEACHER HANDLES A HARD QUESTION.

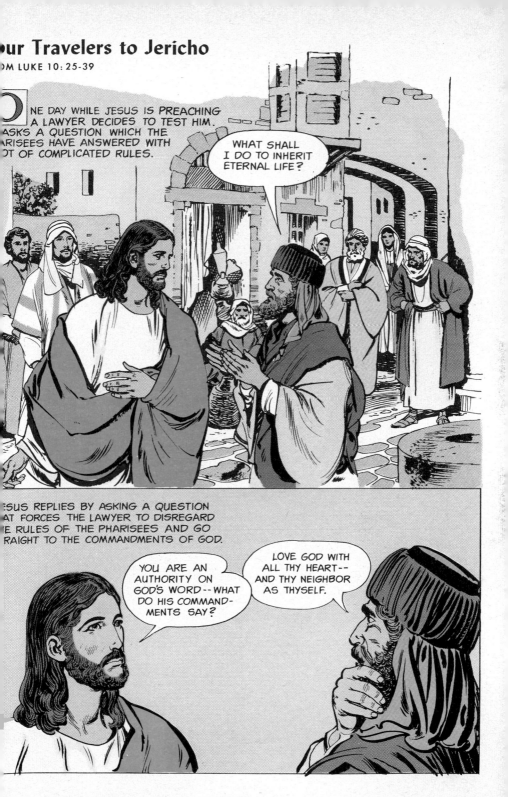

JESUS REPLIES WITH A STORY WHICH FORCES TH LAWYER AGAIN TO ANSWER HIS OWN QUESTION:

A MAN IS TRAVELING FROM JERUSALEM TO JERICHO. ON THE WAY HE IS ATTACKED BY BANDITS, ROBBED, AND LEFT FOR DEAD.

BY CHANCE A PRIEST COMES BY-- HE SEES THE WOUNDED MAN BUT HE QUICKLY PASSES BY.

A LITTLE LATER A LEVITE, AN ASSISTANT TO THE PRIESTS, COMES ALONG-- BUT HE, TO HURRIES BY.

BUT WHEN A SAMARITAN SEES THE INJURED MAN, HE STOPS. ALTHOUGH SAMARITANS ARE BITTER ENEMIES OF THE JEWS, HE BINDS UP THE MAN'S WOUNDS, TAKES HIM TO AN INN, AND PAYS FOR HIS CARE.

WHEN HE FINISHES THE STORY OF THE GOOD SAMARITAN, JESUS ASKS: WHICH ONE OF THE THREE WAS A NEIGHBOR TO THE MAN WHO WAS ROBBED?

THE MAN WHO HELPED HIM.

GO AND DO THE SAME.

THE LAWYER GOES AWAY-- AMAZED AT THE SKILL WITH WHICH JESUS ANSWERED HIS QUESTIONS.

NOW I SEE-- MY NEIGHBOR IS ANYONE WHO NEEDS ME.

JESUS CONTINUES ON HIS PREACHING TOUR. IN BETHANY HE STOPS TO VISIT HIS FRIENDS: MARY, MARTHA, AND LAZARUS. MARY DROPS EVERYTHING SHE IS DOING TO LISTEN TO JESUS...

BUT HER SISTER MARTHA...

IT ISN'T FAIR-- AND I WON'T STAND FOR IT ANY LONGER!

The Lord's Prayer

FROM LUKE 10:40—11:2; MATTHEW 6:9-13;
JOHN 10:22-40; LUKE 15:1-19

WHEN JESUS VISITS IN THE HOME OF HIS FRIENDS, MARY, MARTHA, AND LAZARUS, MARY STOPS HER WORK TO LISTEN TO JESUS. BUT MARTHA HURRIES TO THE KITCHEN TO PREPARE FOOD. AS SHE WORKS SHE BECOMES UPSET BECAUSE MARY DOES NOT HELP HER. AT LAST SHE COMPLAINS TO JESUS.

DON'T YOU THINK IT'S WRONG FOR MARY TO LEAVE ME WITH ALL THE WORK TO DO? TELL HER TO HELP ME.

MARTHA! MARTH YOU ARE WORRY ABOUT TOO MANY ONLY ONE THING IS IMP --TO LEARN THE WILL OF AS MARY HAS CHOSEN T

DURING THE REST OF JESUS' VISIT, MARTHA SEEKS TO LEARN MORE ABOUT GOD. THEN JESUS LEAVES HIS FRIENDS IN BETHANY AND JOINS HIS DISCIPLES FOR A TEACHING TRIP IN JUDEA.

LISTENING TO JESUS MAKES ME FEEL SO CLOSE TO GOD.

DURING HIS TRAVELS JESUS STOPS OFTEN TO PRAY. HIS DISCIPLES SEE THE POWER OF PRAYER IN JESUS' LIFE, AND ONE DAY A DISCIPLE SPEAKS TO HIM ABOUT IT.

TEACH US TO PRAY.

JESUS ANSWERS: WHEN YOU PRAY, SAY,

OUR FATHER WHICH ART IN HEAVEN, HALLOWED BE THY NAME. THY KINGDOM COME. THY WILL BE DONE IN EARTH, AS IT IS IN HEAVEN. GIVE US THIS DAY OUR DAILY BREAD. AND FORGIVE US OUR DEBTS, AS WE FORGIVE OUR DEBTORS. AND LEAD US NOT INTO TEMPTATION, BUT DELIVER US FROM EVIL: FOR THINE IS THE KINGDOM, AND THE POWER, AND THE GLORY, FOR EVER. AMEN.

FOR A MOMENT NO ONE SPEAKS. THEN SOFTLY THE DISCIPLES SAY "AMEN" TO THE SIMPLE PRAYER THAT BECOMES A MODEL FOR THEIR FUTURE PRAYERS TO GOD. AFTER THIS, JESUS AND HIS HELPERS CONTINUE THROUGH JUDEA, PREACHING AND HEALING. BY THE TIME JESUS RETURNS TO JERUSALEM FOR A RELIGIOUS FEAST THE CITY IS FILLED WITH PEOPLE TALKING AND WONDERING ABOUT HIM.

AS JESUS IS WALKING ALONG SOLOMON'S PORCH OF THE TEMPLE, THE PEOPLE SURROUND HIM.

HOW LONG WILL YOU KEEP US WAITING? IF YOU ARE THE MESSIAH, TELL US.

I TOLD YOU, BUT YOU WOULD NOT BELIEVE ME. THE THINGS I HAVE DONE IN MY FATHER'S NAME SHOULD PROVE TO YOU WHO I AM.

DID YOU HEAR THAT? HE CALLED GOD HIS FATHER!

STONE HIM!

JESUS TURNS AND QUIETLY WALKS AWAY, AND--STRANGELY--NO ONE TRIES TO STOP HIM.

JESUS LEAVES JERUSALEM FOR PEREA-- WHERE HE CONTINUES TO PREACH AND HEAL THE SICK. AGAIN THE PHARISEES COMPLAIN BECAUSE HE ASSOCIATES WITH SINNERS. JESUS TELLS THEM A STORY...

A CERTAIN MAN HAS TWO SONS. ONE DAY THE YOUNGER COMES TO HIM.

FATHER, I WANT TO RUN MY OWN LIFE. PLEASE GIVE ME THE SHARE OF YOUR MONEY THAT WILL SOMEDAY BE MINE.

I HAD HOPED YOU WOULD STAY HOME AND HELP WITH THE WORK HERE-- BUT IF YOU WANT THE MONEY, YOU MAY HAVE IT.

THE YOUNG MAN GOES TO ANOTHER COUNTRY-- WHERE HE SPENDS HIS MONEY EATING AND DRINKING WITH BAD COMPANIONS. AT LAST HIS MONEY IS GONE--AND THE ONLY JOB HE CAN GET IS CARING FOR A FARMER'S PIGS.

MY FATHER'S SERVANTS LIVE BETTER THAN THIS! I'M GOING HOME AND ASK MY FATHER TO LET ME WORK FOR HIM--NOT AS HIS SON, BUT AS A SERVANT!

e Prodigal's Return

M LUKE 15:20-32; JOHN 11:1-8

HEN THE PHARISEES COMPLAIN BECAUSE JESUS
ASSOCIATES WITH SINNERS, HE TELLS THEM A
STORY ABOUT A YOUNG MAN WHO LEAVES HOME
YOUNG MAN SPENDS HIS MONEY SO FOOLISHLY THAT
AST HE HAS TO TAKE CARE OF A FARMER'S PIGS
RDER TO KEEP ALIVE. IN HIS MISERY HE DECIDES
O HOME AND WORK FOR HIS FATHER-- NOT
HIS SON, BUT AS ONE OF HIS
VANTS. WHEN HE REACHES
E HIS FATHER RUSHES
TO MEET HIM.

FATHER! I HAVE SINNED AGAINST HEAVEN AND YOU. I'M NO LONGER WORTHY TO BE CALLED YOUR SON.

87

BRING MY SON THE BEST ROBE IN THE HOUSE. AND PREPARE A FEAST, FOR MY SON WHO WAS LOST IS FOUND!

OUT IN THE FIELD THE OLDER SON WORKS HA IO COMPLETE HIS JOB BEFORE NIGHT.

IF MY BROTHER WERE HERE TO HELP, I WOULDN HAVE TO WORK SO MUCH.

THE DAY'S WORK DONE, HE GOES HOME. BUT AS HE APPROACHES THE HOUSE HE HEARS MUSIC...

WHAT'S GOING ON?

YOUR BROTHER HAS RETURNED, AND YOUR FATHER IS HAVING A FEAST FOR HIM.

IN ANGER THE OLDER SON REFUSES TO GO INT(THE HOUSE. SOON HIS FATHER COMES OUT.

YOU HAVE NEVER GIVEN A FEAST FOR ME ALTHOUGH I HAVE STAYED HOME TO HELP YOU. BUT MY BROTHER--

ALL THAT I HAVE IS YOUT MY SON. BUT IT IS RIG FOR US TO BE GLAD FO YOUR BROTHER'S RETUR HE WAS THE SAME AS DE NOW HE IS ALIVE.

89

Called from the Tomb

JOHN 11: 38-54; LUKE 18: 15-23; 19:1-3

BY THE TIME JESUS AND HIS DISCIPLES REACH BETHANY LAZARUS, THE BROTHER OF MARY AND MARTHA, HAS BEEN DEAD FOUR DAYS. AT THE TOMB JESUS ASKS TO HAVE THE STONE ROLLED AWAY. HE PRAYS ALOUD TO GOD, AND THEN CALLS OUT IN A STRONG VOICE...

LAZARUS, COME FORTH.

HE AMAZEMENT OF THE CROWD, 'ARUS APPEARS!

AZARUS!

O JESUS, WE THANK YOU!

N RAISED FROM THE DEAD! THE PEOPLE CAN 'CELY BELIEVE WHAT THEY HAVE SEEN. MANY 'EM TURN TO JESUS CRYING, "MESSIAH! SON OD!" BUT OTHERS GO INTO JERUSALEM TO TELL 'HARISEES WHAT JESUS HAS DONE.

IN ANGER AND DESPERATION THE PHARISEES AND CHIEF PRIESTS CALL A MEETING.

IF NEWS OF THIS GETS AROUND THE PEOPLE WILL TRY TO MAKE JESUS A KING.

AND IF THERE'S A REBELLION THE ROMANS WILL BLAME **US**. WE'LL LOSE OUR POSITIONS AND THE NATION WILL BE DESTROYED.

92

FURTHER ALONG THE WAY JESUS IS STOPPED BY A YOUNG MAN.

TEACHER, WHAT SHALL I DO TO INHERIT ETERNAL LIFE?

KEEP GOD'S COMMANDMENTS.

BUT I HAVE KEPT THE LAWS -- SINCE I WAS A BOY.

YOU NEED TO DO ONE THING MORE -- SELL ALL THAT YOU HAVE, GIVE THE MONEY TO THE POOR, AND FOLLOW ME.

BUT THE YOUNG MAN THINKS TOO MUCH OF HIS RICHES...SLOWLY HE TURNS HIS BACK ON JESUS AND WALKS AWAY.

THE TRAVELERS CONTINUE ON TOWARD JERUSALEM. BY THE TIME THEY REACH JERICHO, JESUS IS IN THE MIDST OF AN EXCITED, HAPPY THRONG.

PLEASE --LET ME THROUGH!

HO--ZACCHEUS, THE CROOKED LITTLE TAX COLLECTOR, WANTS TO SEE JESUS!

I HAVE TO SEE JESUS--AND I WILL!

Man in the Tree
LUKE 19: 4-10; JOHN 12: 1-8; LUKE 19: 29-35

ZACCHEUS, THE WEALTHY TAX COLLECTOR,
IS SO SHORT THAT HE CAN'T LOOK
OVER THE HEADS OF THE PEOPLE. FRANTICALLY
HE RUNS AHEAD OF THE CROWD, CLIMBS A TREE,
AND WAITS. WHEN JESUS
SEES HIM, HE STOPS...

ZACCHEUS, COME DOWN, FOR I WANT TO STAY AT YOUR HOUSE!

ACCHEUS IS AMAZED THAT JESUS WOULD
VEN SPEAK TO HIM, BUT HE CLIMBS DOWN
T ONCE AND LEADS THE WAY TO HIS HOUSE.

WHY WOULD A TEACHER AS GREAT AS JESUS WANT TO STAY WITH THAT CROOKED LITTLE TAX COLLECTOR?

ZACCHEUS WONDERS, TOO, BUT HE SOON
DISCOVERS THAT BEING IN THE PRESENCE
OF JESUS MAKES HIM ASHAMED OF EVERY
WRONG THING HE HAS EVER DONE. HE
WANTS TO BE FORGIVEN AND START OVER...

HALF OF MY GOODS I WILL GIVE TO THE POOR. AND IF I HAVE CHEATED ANYONE I WILL PAY HIM BACK FOUR TIMES AS MUCH.

SALVATION HAS COME TO YOU TODAY, ZACCHEUS. IT IS TO HELP PEOPLE LIKE YOU THAT I HAVE COME TO THE WORLD.

ROM JERICHO THE CROWDS CONTINUE THEIR WAY TO JERUSALEM FOR THE GREAT PASSOVER FEAST. THE FESTIVAL IS STILL SIX DAYS AWAY, SO JESUS STOPS IN BETHANY TO VISIT HIS FRIENDS -- MARY, MARTHA, AND LAZARUS. AT A SUPPER IN THE HOME OF SIMON THE LEPER, MARY KNEELS BESIDE JESUS AND ANOINTS HIS FEET WITH COSTLY OIL -- THEN WIPES THEM WITH HER HAIR.

JDAS ISCARIOT, TREASURER OF THE DISCIPLES,
ANGERED BY WHAT HE THINKS IS A
ASTE OF MONEY.

WHY WASN'T THE OIL SOLD AND THE MONEY GIVEN TO THE POOR?

I WANTED TO HONOR JESUS--

LET HER ALONE, SHE IS SHOWING HER LOVE FOR ME.

JUDAS IS ANGERED BY THIS REPRIMAND--
AND AN UGLY THOUGHT COMES TO HIS MIND.

WHEN THE TIME IS RIGHT I'LL GO TO THE PRIESTS AND PHARISEES-- **THEY'LL** BE GLAD TO LISTEN TO ME.

THE NEXT DAY JESUS AND HIS DISCIPLES JOIN THE CROWDS GOING UP TO JERUSALEM TO PREPARE FOR THE PASSOVER FEAST. ON THE WAY...

GO OVER INTO THAT VILLAGE AND AS YOU ENTER YOU WILL FIND A COLT. BRING IT TO ME. AND IF ANYONE QUESTIONS YOU, TELL HIM I NEED THE ANIMAL-- AND WILL RETURN IT.

PUZZLED, THE TWO DISCIPLES GO TO THE VILLAGE WHERE THEY FIND THE COLT. WHEN THEY START TO UNTIE THE ROPE...

WHAT DO YOU MEAN, TAKING MY ANIMAL?

JESUS SAID TO TELL YOU THAT HE NEEDED IT.

AT THE MENTION OF JESUS' NAME THE MAN GLADLY GIVES HIS CONSENT

I WONDER WHY JESUS WANTS MY COLT. IT HAS NEVER BEEN RIDDEN-- BESIDES, IT'S NOT A VERY NOBLE BEAST FOR ANYONE AS IMPORTANT AS JESUS TO RIDE.

Triumphal Entry

LUKE 19:36-38; MATTHEW 21:10-17

IT IS THE FIRST DAY OF THE WEEK. THE ROAD TO JERUSALEM IS FILLED WITH PEOPLE ON THE WAY TO CELEBRATE THE PASSOVER FEAST OF THE JEWS. AT JESUS' REQUEST HIS DISCIPLES BRING HIM A LOWLY BEAST OF BURDEN -- HE MOUNTS IT AND JOINS THE MULTITUDE OF PILGRIMS. EAGERLY THEY MAKE WAY FOR HIM -- WAVING PALM BRANCHES AND CARPETING HIS PATH WITH THEIR GARMENTS. AND, WHILE THEY ESCORT HIM -- TRIUMPHANTLY -- UP THE ROAD AND INTO THE CITY, THE SOUND OF THEIR PRAISES FILLS THE AIR: "HOSANNA! BLESSED IS THE KING THAT COMETH IN THE NAME OF THE LORD!"

98

99

When Jesus begins to preach, people crowd into the temple courts to hear him. But behind closed doors the priests and pharisees plot their strategy. By Tuesday they are ready...

QUIETLY JESUS RETURNS THE COIN.

GIVE TO CAESAR THE THINGS THAT ARE HIS, AND TO GOD THE THINGS THAT ARE GOD'S.

THE PHARISEES ARE ANGRY AT BEING DEFEATE AGAIN, BUT THEY MARVEL AT JESUS' SKILL IN HANDLING THEIR TRICK QUESTION. LATER IN THE DAY ONE OF THEM ASKS ANOTHER DIFFICULT QUESTION.

WHICH OF OUR 613 COMMAND- MENTS IS THE MOST IMPORTANT?

THOU SHALT LOVE THE LORD THY GOD WITH ALL THY HEART, AND WITH ALL THY SOUL, AND WITH ALL THY MIND, AND WITH ALL THY STRENGTH. AND THE SECOND IS THIS: THOU SHALT LOVE THY NEIGHBOR AS THYSELF.

YOU HAVE SPOKEN THE TRUTH. TO LOVE GOD AND ONE'S NEIGHBOR IS MORE IMPORTANT THAN ALL BURNT OFFERINGS.

YOU ARE NOT FAR FROM THE KINGDOM OF GOD.

THEN JESUS WARNS THE PEOPLE AGAINST THOSE WHO DO GOOD DEEDS JUST TO BE SEEN BY OTHERS. WHEN HE HAS FINISHED SPEAKING HE LOOKS UP TO SEE A PROUD MAN PLACE A LARGE SUM OF MONEY IN THE TEMPLE TREASURY.

THE MAN IS FOLLOWED BY A POOR WIDOW WHO HUMBLY DROPS IN TWO SMALL COINS.

THE WIDOW HAS GIVEN MORE THAN ANYONE ELSE -- FOR SHE HAS GIVEN ALL SHE HAS TO GOD.

WITH THESE WORDS JESUS LEAVES THE TEMPLE -- FOR THE LAST TIME. OUTSIDE JERUSALEM, ON THE QUIET SLOPES OF THE MOUNT OF OLIVES, SOME OF HIS DISCIPLES ASK ABOUT THE FUTURE. JESUS EXPLAINS THAT HIS GOSPEL WILL BE PREACHED THROUGHOUT THE WORLD -- AND THEN HE WILL COME AGAIN TO JUDGE THE WORLD.

JESUS AND HIS DISCIPLES RETURN TO BETHANY. LATER THAT NIGHT JUDAS HURRIES TO JERUSALEM TO CARRY OUT AN IDEA THAT CAME TO HIM WHEN MARY ANOINTED JESUS WITH COSTLY OIL.

I WANT TO SEE THE CHIEF PRIEST.

A MAN NAMED JUDAS ISCARIOT WANTS TO SEE YOU. HE SAYS IT'S URGENT.

JUDAS ISCARIOT? WHY HE'S ONE OF JESUS' DISCIPLES SHOW HIM IN.

I KNOW HOW MUCH YOU WANT TO GET RID OF JESUS. WHAT WILL YOU GIVE TO HAVE HIM DELIVERED TO YOU -- AWAY FROM THE CROWDS THAT BELIEVE IN HIM?

THIRTY PIECES OF SILVER.

IS LATE TUESDAY NIGHT WHEN
JDAS BARGAINS WITH THE CHIEF
RIESTS TO BETRAY JESUS. AFTER
AGREEMENT IS MADE HE RETURNS
ETHANY AND SPENDS WEDNESDAY
JESUS AND THE DISCIPLES--
R SUSPECTING THAT JESUS
WS WHAT HE HAS DONE.
RSDAY, JESUS CALLS
R AND JOHN ASIDE.

GO INTO JERUSALEM
AND MAKE THINGS READY
FOR THE PASSOVER
FEAST.

RE CAN WE GO
THAT YOUR
MIES WILL
SEE US?

WHEN YOU ENTER THE
CITY YOU WILL SEE A
MAN CARRYING A PITCHER.
FOLLOW HIM AND ASK HIS
MASTER TO SHOW YOU
THE ROOM THAT WE
MAY USE.

PETER AND JOHN GO AT ONCE TO JERUSALEM. THEY
FIND THE SERVANT CARRYING A PITCHER AND FOL-
LOW HIM HOME

WHERE IS THE ROOM
IN WHICH JESUS AND HIS
DISCIPLES CAN EAT THE
PASSOVER?

COME
WITH ME.

THE MAN LEADS THEM QUICKLY UP THE STAIRS TO A BIG UPPER ROOM.

I'M HONORED TO HAVE JESUS CELEBRATE THE PASSOVER IN MY HOUSE.

PETER AND JOHN PREPARE FOR THE FEAST, AND THAT EVENING JESUS JOINS THE TWELVE IN THE UPPER ROOM. AFTER THEY ARE SEATED JESUS KNEELS, LIKE A SERVANT, TO WASH THE FEET OF HIS DISCIPLES.

NO, LORD. I'M NOT GOOD ENOUGH TO HAVE **YOU** WAIT ON ME!

IF YOU DO NOT LET ME SERVE YOU, PETER YOU WILL HAVE NO PLACE IN MY KINGDOM.

ER JESUS HAS WASHED ALL OF THE DISCIPLES' , HE SITS DOWN AT THE TABLE AGAIN.

IF I, YOUR LORD AND MASTER, HAVE SERVED YOU, YOU SHOULD DO THE SAME FOR ONE ANOTHER. THE SERVANT IS NOT GREATER THAN HIS MASTER.

AFTER A FEW MINUTES JESUS MAKES A STARTLING STATEMENT.

ONE OF YOU IS GOING TO BETRAY ME.

BETRAY YOU? IS IT I, LORD?

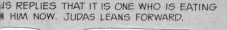
S REPLIES THAT IT IS ONE WHO IS EATING HIM NOW. JUDAS LEANS FORWARD.

S IT I?

YOU HAVE SAID IT. WHAT YOU ARE GOING TO DO, JUDAS, DO QUICKLY.

AT ONCE THE TRAITOR RISES FROM THE TABLE AND HURRIES AWAY. BUT THE OTHER DISCIPLES DO NOT UNDERSTAND WHY...

THE DISCIPLES ARE FRIGHTENED AT THE THOUGHT OF JESUS LEAVING THEM.

QUIETLY, THEY LEAVE THE UPPER ROOM. THEY WALK THROUGH THE MOONLIT STREETS OF THE CITY, OUT AN EAST GATE, AND ACROSS A VALLEY TO THE GARDEN OF GETHSEMANE ON THE MOUNT OF OLIVES.

AT THE ENTRANCE JESUS ASKS EIGHT OF THE DISCIPLES TO WAIT WHILE HE TAKES HIS CLOSEST DISCIPLES, PETER, JAMES, AND JOHN FARTHER INTO THE GARDEN.

THIS IS A SAD NIGHT FOR ME -- STAY HERE AND WATCH WHILE I GO ALONE TO PRAY.

O MY FATHER, IF THOU BE WILLING, REMOVE THIS AGONY FROM ME; NEVERTHELESS, NOT MY WILL, BUT THINE BE DONE.

WHEN JESUS RETURNS TO HIS DISCIPLES, HE FINDS THEM SLEEPING. TWO MORE TIMES HE GOES ASIDE TO PRAY, AND EACH TIME HE FINDS HIS FRIENDS ASLEEP. AFTER WAKING THEM THE THIRD TIME...

ARISE -- THE ONE WHO IS TO BETRAY ME IS NEAR.

Tried–and Denied!

MATTHEW 26:57-75; JOHN 18:28-38; LUKE 23:6-12

FOLLOWING HIS ARREST, JESUS IS BROUGHT TO THE PALACE OF THE HIGH PRIEST. FALSE WITNESSES BOLDLY ACCUSE HIM OF MANY THINGS --BUT THEY CAN PROVE NOTHING. FINALLY THE HIGH PRIEST QUESTIONS THE PRISONER.

ARE YOU THE CHRIST, THE SON OF GOD?

I AM.

THERE! YOU HEARD HIM. ANYONE WHO SPEAKS BLASPHEMY BY CLAIMING TO BE GOD'S SON DESERVES TO DIE.

INSTANTLY THE GUARDS TURN ON JESUS -- SPITTING ON HIM, COVERING HIS FACE AND DEMANDING THAT HE PROVE HIS POWER BY IDENTIFYING THOSE WHO STRIKE HIM.

112

WHILE JESUS IS SUFFERING THESE INSULTS, PETER -- WHO HAS SECRETLY FOLLOWED HIM INTO THE CITY -- WARMS HIS HANDS BY A FIRE IN THE PALACE COURTYARD. WHILE HE IS TALKING, A MAID STOPS AND LOOKS AT HIM...

YOU WERE ONE OF THOSE WITH JESUS OF NAZARETH.

ME? I DON'T KNOW WHAT YOU'RE TALKING ABOUT.

AFRAID OF BEING QUESTIONED FURTHER, PETER GOES OUT INTO THE HALLWAY, BUT THERE...

THIS FELLOW WAS WITH JESUS.

JESUS? I DON'T EVEN KNOW THE MAN.

ABOUT AN HOUR LATER SOME MEN APPROACH PETER.

DIDN'T I SEE YOU IN THE GARDEN WHEN THE SOLDIERS TOOK JESUS?

YOU ARE A GALILEAN LIKE JESUS. I CAN TELL BY THE WAY YOU TALK.

113

FOR THE THIRD TIME PETER DENIES KNOWING JESUS-- AND THEN THE COCK CROWS! STARTLED, PETER RAISES HIS HEAD--TO LOOK STRAIGHT INTO THE EYES OF JESUS, WHO IS BEING LED OUT OF THE COURT.

SICK WITH SHAME, PETER RUSHES OUTSIDE, WEEPING BITTERLY.

THREE TIMES I DENIED MY LORD--JUST AS HE SAID I WOULD! O GOD FORGIVE ME, FORGIVE ME!

IN THE EARLY HOURS OF FRIDAY MORNING THE MEMBERS OF THE JEWISH HIGH COURT, WHICH CANNOT SENTENCE A MAN TO DEATH, TAKE JESUS TO THE ROMAN GOVERNOR, PILATE. CLEVERLY, THEY CHARGE HIM-- NOT WITH BREAKING JEWISH LAWS--BUT WITH TREASON AGAINST ROME. PILATE QUESTIONS JESUS PRIVATELY AND THEN RETURNS HIM TO THE PRIESTS AND CROWDS THAT HAVE GATHERED OUTSIDE.

I DO NOT FIND THIS MAN GUILTY OF ANY CRIME.

114

NOT GUILTY? WHY, HE TRIED TO START REVOLTS ALL OVER JUDEA AND GALILEE!

AT THE MENTION OF GALILEE, PILATE SENDS JESUS TO HEROD, THE RULER OF GALILEE, WHO IS IN JERUSALEM FOR THE PASSOVER. HEROD IS CURIOUS AND ASKS JESUS TO PERFORM SOME MIRACLE. WHEN JESUS WILL NOT, HEROD AND HIS SOLDIERS MAKE FUN OF HIM--AND THEN RETURN HIM TO PILATE.

PILATE IS TRAPPED. [HE] DOES NOT BELIEVE [JE]SUS IS GUILTY OF [TR]EASON. "BUT, IF I [LET] HIM GO," HE [AR]GUES TO HIMSELF, ["AN]D THE JEWISH [LEA]DERS MAKE [TRO]UBLE, THE [EM]PEROR IN ROME [WIL]L HOLD ME [RE]SPONSIBLE." [FIN]ALLY HE THINKS [OF] A WAY TO EASE [HIS] CONSCIENCE [AN]D PROTECT [HIM]SELF...

THE PEOPLE! I'LL LET THEM DECIDE!

Condemned to Die

JOHN 18:39—19:16; MATTHEW 27:3-10

THE JEWISH LEADERS HAVE CHARGED JESUS WITH TREASON AGAINST ROME. PILATE, THE ROMAN GOVERNOR, DOES NOT BELIEVE HE IS GUILTY--BUT HE IS AFRAID TO ANGER THE JEWS FOR FEAR THEY WILL STIR UP SO MUCH TROUBLE THAT THE REPORTS OF IT WILL REACH THE EMPEROR IN ROME. LOOKING AT THE CROWDS IN JERUSALEM FOR THE PASSOVER, HE SUDDENLY SEES A WAY OUT: LET THE PEOPLE DECIDE WHETHER OR NOT JESUS SHOULD DIE. BUT HE DOES NOT KNOW THAT THE PRIESTS ARE STIRRING UP THE CROWDS AGAINST JESUS.

IT IS THE CUSTOM TO RELEASE A PRISONER TO YOU DURING THE PASSOVER. WHICH SHALL I GIVE YOU-- JESUS, WHO IS CALLED THE CHRIST-- OR BARABBAS, THE MURDERER?

BARABBAS! GIVE US BARABBAS!

PILATE IS STUNNED. HE MAKES ANOTHER ATTEMPT TO SAVE JESUS.

SCOURGE HIM.

MAYBE THE PEOPLE WILL BE SATISFIED IF THE PRISONER IS PUNISHED.

SO JESUS IS WHIPPED WITH LEATHER THONGS. THEN, IN SPORT, THE SOLDIERS MAKE A CROWN OF THORNS AND PLACE IT ON HIS HEAD.

HAIL, THE KING OF THE JEWS!

HOPING THE SIGHT OF JESUS, BRUTALLY BEATEN, WILL AROUSE THE CROWD'S SYMPATHY, PILATE PRESENTS HIM TO THE MULTITUDE.

BEHOLD THE MAN!

CRUCIFY HIM!

CRUCIFY HIM!

BY THIS TIME EVEN PILATE IS SICKENED AT THE SIGHT OF SUCH HATE. BUT, NOT WILLING TO ENDANGER HIS POSITION FURTHER, HE SURRENDERS JESUS TO BE CRUCIFIED. AS HE DOES SO HE WRITES AN INSCRIPTION TO BE PLACED ON JESUS' CROSS.

JESUS OF NAZARETH, THE KING OF THE JEWS.

IT IS PILATE'S REVENGE. HE KNOWS THAT THE JEWISH LEADERS WILL BURN WITH RAGE TO SEE THOSE WORDS ON THE CROSS OF A MAN THEY HAVE CONDEMNED TO DIE.

NO! NO! DON'T WRITE THAT HE IS THE KING OF THE JEWS. WRITE THAT HE SAID, "I AM KING OF THE JEWS."

WHAT I HAVE WRITTEN, I HAVE WRITTEN.

TO JESUS, THE HOURS FROM THE TIME HE WAS ARRESTED UNTIL HE IS SENTENCED TO BE CRUCIFIED HAVE BEEN FILLED WITH AGONY.

SOMETIME DURING THOSE DARK HOURS THE TRAITOR, JUDAS, REALIZES WHAT HE HAS DONE AND RUSHES TO THE CHIEF PRIESTS...

119

A King Is Crucified

LUKE 23:26-46; JOHN 19:25-27

HAPPY, EXCITED PILGRIMS FROM ALL OVER PALESTINE HAVE BEEN CROWDING INTO JERUSALEM FOR DAYS TO CELEBRATE THE PASSOVER FEAST. BUT ON FRIDAY MORNING STARTLING NEWS SWEEPS ACROSS THE CITY LIKE A CHILLING WIND: JESUS OF NAZARETH IS GOING TO BE CRUCIFIED -- FOR TREASON!

THE STREET THAT LEADS TO THE HILL OF EXECUTION IS SOON FILLED WITH A STRANGE MIXTURE OF PEOPLE -- PRIESTS AND PHARISEES WHO DEMAND JESUS' DEATH; WOMEN WEEPING FOR THE MAN WHO FORGAVE SINS AND HEALED THE SICK; AND THE CURIOUS WHO WANT ONLY TO SEE A CONDEMNED MAN CARRY HIS CROSS...

...THE WAY JESUS FALLS UNDER THE WEIGHT ...THE HEAVY CROSS. TO KEEP THE UGLY ...CESSION MOVING, THE ROMAN OFFICER ...ES A BYSTANDER, SIMON FROM ...ENE.

HERE-- YOU CARRY THIS CROSS!

IT IS ABOUT NINE O'CLOCK WHEN JESUS, AND TWO ROBBERS WHO ARE TO BE CRUCIFIED WITH HIM, REACH CALVARY. AND THERE THE SON OF GOD IS NAILED TO A CROSS. ABOVE HIS HEAD IS FASTENED A SIGN: JESUS OF NAZARETH, THE KING OF THE JEWS!

FATHER, FORGIVE THEM: FOR THEY KNOW NOT WHAT THEY DO.

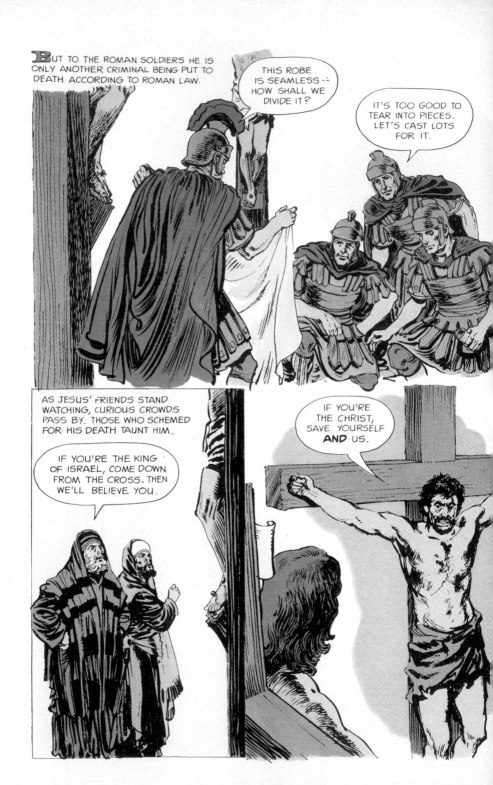

BUT TO THE ROMAN SOLDIERS HE IS ONLY ANOTHER CRIMINAL BEING PUT TO DEATH ACCORDING TO ROMAN LAW.

THIS ROBE IS SEAMLESS -- HOW SHALL WE DIVIDE IT?

IT'S TOO GOOD TO TEAR INTO PIECES. LET'S CAST LOTS FOR IT.

AS JESUS' FRIENDS STAND WATCHING, CURIOUS CROWDS PASS BY. THOSE WHO SCHEMED FOR HIS DEATH TAUNT HIM.

IF YOU'RE THE KING OF ISRAEL, COME DOWN FROM THE CROSS. THEN WE'LL BELIEVE YOU.

IF YOU'RE THE CHRIST, SAVE YOURSELF **AND** US.

The Sealed Tomb
MARK 15:38, 39; LUKE 23:48, 49;
JOHN 19:38-42; MATTHEW 27:62-66

AT ABOUT NINE O'CLOCK FRIDAY MORNING JESUS OF NAZARETH IS CRUCIFIED OUTSIDE THE WALLS OF JERUSALEM. FROM NOON UNTIL THREE O'CLOCK DARKNESS COVERS THE LAND. THEN -- SUDDENLY - AN EARTHQUAKE ROCKS THE GROUND. AND IN JERUSALEM ...

THE VEIL BEFORE THE HOLIEST PLACE IN THE TEMPLE HAS BEEN RIPPED! WHAT CAN IT MEAN?

THE ANSWER IS THAT ON A HILL CALLED CALVARY THE SON OF GOD HAS GIVEN HIS LIFE TO PAY FOR THE SINS OF THE WORLD. THE VEIL IN THE TEMPLE NO LONGER SEPARATES MAN FROM THE PRESENCE OF GOD, FOR JESUS, THE SON, HAS OPENED THE WAY TO GOD, THE FATHER.

OUTSIDE THE CITY, EVEN THE ROMAN OFFICER WHO DIRECTED THE CRUCIFIXION IS AWED BY WHAT HAS HAPPENED. REVERENTLY, HE LOOKS UP AT THE MAN WHO FORGAVE HIS ENEMIES.

TRULY THIS MAN WAS GOD'S SON!

THE PEOPLE, TOO, ARE SHAKEN BY THE EXECUTION. AS THEY TURN BACK TO THE CITY...

I HAD HOPED THAT HE WAS THE ONE WHO WOULD DELIVER US FROM THE ROMANS.

IN JERUSALEM JOSEPH OF ARIMATHEA, A MEMBER OF THE JEWISH HIGH COURT AND SECRETLY A FOLLOWER OF JESUS, GOES BOLDLY TO PILATE.

MAY I HAVE THE BODY OF JESUS SO THAT WE MAY BURY IT BEFORE THE SABBATH?

YES... I'LL GIVE ORDERS TO MY OFFICER IN CHARGE.

REVERENTLY, JOSEPH TAKES THE BODY OF JESUS FROM THE CROSS. THEN HE AND HIS FRIEND, NICODEMUS, WRAP IT IN LINEN CLOTH, AND PLACE IT IN JOSEPH'S GARDEN TOMB.

EARLY THE NEXT DAY THE PRIESTS AND PHARISE ALSO GO TO PILATE...

WE REMEMBER JESUS SAID THAT AFTER THREE DAYS HE WOULD RISE FROM THE DEAD. ORDER YOUR SOLDIERS TO SEAL AND GUARD THE TOMB SO THAT HIS DISCIPLES CAN'T STEAL THE BODY AND CLAIM THAT JESUS MADE GOOD ON HIS BOAST.

TAKE THE SOLDIERS YOU NEED AND SET UP A GUARD UNTIL AFTER THE THIRD DAY.

SO THE TOMB IS SEALED, AND ROMAN SOLDIERS ARE PLACED ON GUARD.

THERE-- THAT'S THE LAST WE'LL HEAR OF THIS MAN WHO CALLED HIMSELF THE SON OF GOD!

RK 16:1-7; JOHN 20:2-18; MATTHEW 28:11-15;
E 24:13-32

RIDAY -- JUST OUTSIDE JERUSALEM -- JESUS OF NAZARETH IS CRUCIFIED AND BURIED. AT THE REQUEST OF THE PRIESTS AND PHARISEES, THE TOMB IS SEALED AND ROMAN SOLDIERS ET TO GUARD IT.

BUT ON THE MORNING OF THE THIRD DAY THE EARTH TREMBLES. AN ANGEL OF THE LORD DESCENDS -- AND ROLLS THE HEAVY STONE ASIDE. TERRIFIED, THE SOLDIERS FALL TO THE GROUND. WHEN THEY CAN GET TO THEIR FEET THEY RUSH BACK TO THE CITY.

HAT SAME MORNING MARY MAGDALENE AND OTHER FRIENDS F JESUS HURRY TO THE OMB WITH SPICES TO NOINT HIS BODY. N THE WAY, THEY ORRY ABOUT HOW HEY WILL GET THE TONE ROLLED WAY. BUT WHEN HEY REACH THE ARDEN...

THE TOMB! IT IS OPEN!

127

IN THE CITY PETER AND JOHN ARE SO STARTLED BY MARY'S NEWS THAT THEY RACE BACK AHEAD OF HER. WHEN THEY REACH THE TOMB--

BY THE TIME MARY REACHES THE GARDEN THE OTHERS HAVE GONE. IN HER GRIEF SHE DOES NOT RECOGNIZE THE VOICE OF ONE WHO QUESTIONS HER.

FTLY JESUS SPEAKS HER NAME--
ARY!" SHE TURNS--AND SEES HER
EN LORD.

MASTER!

BUT JESUS' FRIENDS ARE NOT THE ONLY ONES WHO ARE EXCITED ABOUT WHAT HAPPENED IN THE GARDEN. IN JERUSALEM THE ROMAN SOLDIERS REPORT TO THE PRIESTS AND PHARISEES. AFRAID OF WHAT MAY HAPPEN IF THE TRUTH IS KNOWN, THEY ACT QUICKLY.

HERE, TAKE THIS MONEY. TELL PEOPLE THAT JESUS' DISCIPLES STOLE HIS BODY.

HILE THE SOLDIERS SPREAD
EIR LIE, JESUS JOINS TWO OF
5 DISCIPLES ON THE WAY TO
MMAUS. THEY TALK WITH HIM,
JT THEY DO NOT KNOW WHO HE IS.

THAT EVENING AS THEY DINE IN EMMAUS, JESUS BLESSES THE BREAD--AND WHEN HE HANDS IT TO THEM THEY SUDDENLY RECOGNIZE HIM.

JESUS!

AND JUST AS SUDDENLY HE VANISHES FROM THEIR SIGHT!

Behind Locked Doors

LUKE 24:33-43; JOHN 20:19—21:6

IT IS LATE SUNDAY NIGHT-- THROUGHOUT JERUSALEM PEOPLE ARE STILL TALKING ABOUT THE STRANGE REPORT OF THE ROMAN SOLDIERS.

THEY SAY JESUS' DISCIPLES STOLE HIS BODY TO MAKE US BELIEVE HE ROSE FROM THE DEAD.

I WONDER WHAT THOSE BRAVE ROMAN GUARDS WERE DOING WHILE THE TOMB WAS ROBBED. AND WHAT DO THE DISCIPLES SAY?

BUT JESUS' FRIENDS HAVE ALSO HEARD THE SOLDIERS' REPORT. THEY ARE AFRAID THEY MAY BE ARRESTED, SO THEY LOCK THE DOORS IN THE UPPER ROOM WHERE ALL -- BUT THOMAS -- HAVE GATHERED. TWO FRIENDS FIND THEM THERE.

JESUS IS ALIVE! WE WERE ON OUR WAY TO EMMAUS WHEN A STRANGER JOINED US. WE ASKED HIM TO HAVE SUPPER WITH US. AND WHEN HE BLESSED THE BREAD AND GAVE IT TO US, WE KNEW--ALL AT ONCE -- THAT THE STRANGER WAS JESUS. THEN HE DISAPPEARED.

131

A WEEK LATER THOMAS IS WITH THE DISCIPLES WHEN THEY MEET AGAIN BEHIND LOCKED DOORS. ONCE MORE JESUS APPEARS TO THEM.

THOMAS, TOUCH MY HANDS AND MY SIDE.

MY LORD AND MY GOD!

BECAUSE YOU HAVE SEEN, THOMAS, YOU BELIEVE. BLESSED ARE THOSE WHO HAVE NOT SEEN AND YET HAVE BELIEVED.

AGAIN JESUS DISAPPEARS FROM THEIR SIGHT.

OBEYING A COMMAND THAT JESUS HAD GIVEN THEM, THE DISCIPLES GO NORTH TO GALILEE. ONE EVENING THEY GO FISHING. THEY FISH ALL NIGHT BUT CATCH NOTHING. AT DAYBREAK THEY SEE THE FIGURE OF A MAN STANDING ON THE SHORE.

CAST YOUR NET ON THE RIGHT SIDE OF THE BOAT.

THEY OBEY—AND SUDDENLY THE NET IS SO FULL OF FISH THEY CANNOT PULL IT IN.

The Last Command

JOHN 21:7-18; MATTHEW 28:16-20; LUKE 24:44-51

ALL NIGHT THE DISCIPLES OF JESUS FISH IN THE SEA OF GALILEE--AND CATCH NOTHING. AT DAYBREAK THEY SEE A MAN ON SHORE WHO TELLS THEM TO CAST THEIR NET ON THE RIGHT SIDE OF THE BOAT. THEY OBEY--AND SUDDENLY THE NET IS SO FULL THAT THE RUGGED FISHERMEN CANNOT DRAW IT UP. JOHN LOOKS AGAIN AT THE FIGURE ON THE SHORE...

LOOK, PETER, IT IS THE LORD!

PETER IS SO EAGER TO REACH JESUS THAT HE JUMPS INTO THE WATER AND SWIMS TO LAND. THE OTHERS BRING THE BOAT IN AND ANCHOR IT OFFSHORE. AFTER THE NET IS PULLED IN, JESUS CALLS TO HIS HUNGRY DISCIPLES.

COME AND EAT.

WHEN THEY FINISH EATING, JESUS TURNS TO PETER.

PETER, DO YOU LOVE ME?

YES, LORD, YOU KNOW I DO.

TWICE MORE JESUS ASKS PETER THE SAME QUESTION, AND EACH TIME PETER DECLARES HIS LOYALTY. THEN JESUS GIVES HIM A GREAT ASSIGNMENT.

TAKE CARE OF MY FOLLOWERS, PETER.

A FEW DAYS LATER JESUS APPEARS TO FIVE HUNDRED OF HIS FOLLOWERS, GATHERED AT HIS COMMAND, ON A MOUNTAIN NEAR THE SEA OF GALILEE. HE GIVES THEM A GREAT COMMISSION:

GO YE THEREFORE, AND TEACH ALL NATIONS, BAPTIZING THEM IN THE NAME OF THE FATHER, AND OF THE SON, AND OF THE HOLY SPIRIT, TEACHING THEM TO OBSERVE ALL THINGS WHATSOEVER I HAVE COMMANDED YOU: AND, LO, I AM WITH YOU ALWAYS, EVEN UNTO THE END OF THE WORLD.

OLLOWING THIS, THE ELEVEN
DISCIPLES RETURN TO
JERUSALEM. THERE JESUS
MEETS WITH THEM AND
EXPLAINS HOW--BY HIS
DEATH AND RESURRECTION--
HAS FULFILLED GOD'S MISSION
HIM TO BE THE SAVIOR OF
WORLD. HE CHARGES THEM
CARRY ON THE WORK.
T WAIT IN JERUSALEM,"
ADDS, "UNTIL THE POWER
GOD'S HOLY SPIRIT
MES UPON YOU."

THE FORTIETH DAY
ER HIS RESURRECTION,
US TAKES HIS DISCIPLES
THE MOUNT OF OLIVES
R BETHANY. AND WHILE
IS BLESSING THEM, HE
ENDS INTO HEAVEN.